EVERTON QUIZ BOOK

THE EVERTON QUIZ BOOK

Compiled by
Alex Hosie

MAINSTREAM
PUBLISHING

First published in 1987 by
MAINSTREAM PUBLISHING COMPANY (EDINBURGH) LTD.
7 Albany Street
Edinburgh EH1 3UG

British Library Cataloguing in Publication Data:
Hosie, Alex
    The Everton Quiz Book.
    1. Everton Football Club — Miscellanea
    I. Title
    796.334'63'0942753   GV943.6.E93

    ISBN 1 85158 093 X

Typeset in Ehrhardt by Pulse Origination, Edinburgh.
Printed in Great Britain by Butler & Tanner, Frome, Somerset.

Acknowledgements

We would like to thank Terry Mealey for his assistance in providing pictures for this publication.

While every care has been taken to ensure accuracy, the publishers and author cannot accept responsibility for any errors which may have occurred in this publication.

Contents

QUESTIONS

ANSWERS

Questions

1 Arsenal were the first team to win at Goodison in the League in October, by 1-0. What was unusual about their goal?

2 How much did Ian Snodin cost from Leeds United?

3 Who scored his ninth goal against Manchester United in a televised match in September 1986?

4 Who did Everton play in a testimonial match for Paul Power?

5 Which Everton player scored an unusual 'hat-trick' during the League campaign?

6 In the Littlewoods Cup quarter-final match against Liverpool which Everton lost 0-1, who were Everton's two substitutes?

7 Which Sheffield Wednesday player was sent off at Goodison as Everton won 3-0 in the Littlewoods Cup third round?

8 When Everton beat Queens Park Rangers 1-0 at Loftus Road in January why was the victory special?

9 Who did Everton beat in the first League match of the season by 2-0 thanks to a Kevin Sheedy double?

10 What part did Kenny Dalglish play in Everton's team selection for the Screen Sport Super Cup final, which had been held over from the previous season?

11 Who scored Everton's goal in the Charity Shield draw with Liverpool?

12 What was special about Graeme Sharp's hat-trick when Everton beat Newcastle 5-2 in the Full Members Cup third round?

13 How much did Everton pay Norwich for Dave Watson?

14 Who scored a double in the second round first leg of the Littlewoods Cup against Newport, and what was the aggregate score in the tie?

15 When Everton won 1-0 at Bradford in the FA Cup fourth round, who scored the goal?

16 Everton had to beat them on a January Sunday to stay top of the League but lost 0-1. Who were the team?

17 Formerly on the books of Liverpool, he scored the only goal of the match as Everton lost at Luton. Name the player?

18 Everton scored nine goals in three days over Christmas. Can you name their two opponents?

19 When Everton beat the then League leaders Wimbledon 2-1 in

The 1987 League Champions with the trophy.

London in September, what happened when Alan Cork equalised for the Dons?

20 Who did Everton beat in the third round of the FA Cup?

REMEMBER THIS SEASON—1914/15

Obviously not too many people will remember, but for fans and historians the season was one of great importance as the Blues won the League title for only the second time in their history and reached the semi-finals of the FA Cup. It was an era of great Everton players like Harry Makepeace and Tom Fleetwood, so it's worth seeing what you know about the year which saw the world go to war.

21 Who was Everton's top scorer during the season?

22 Which London team did Everton beat 2-1 in the third round of the Cup?

23 Everton lost both League games to two other Lancashire teams. Can you name either of them?

23 Who was Everton's regular goalkeeper of the period?

25 Can you name the 17-year-old who made his Everton debut in a League match against Manchester City?

26 Which team did Everton beat 3-0 in the first round of the FA Cup?

27 At which ground did Everton contest the FA Cup semi-final?

28 Name the Scot who was the regular right-back during this season?

29 He was signed from Rochdale, his regular position was wing-half, he played a game at centre-forward against West Bromwich and scored. Who?

30 Everton won the League title, but which other Lancashire team finished runners-up to the Blues?

31 Who was the Scot who occupied the centre-half position with some distinction at this time?

32 In the second round of the FA Cup Everton won 4-0 at Goodison against which team?

33 In which League game did Bobby Parker hit all of Everton's four goals?

34 How many times did Bobby Parker hit a hat-trick or more during the season?

35 Who beat Everton 2-0 in the FA Cup semi-final?

36 Who scored a double for Everton against Barnsley in the FA Cup first round?

37 He scored on his Everton debut the previous season and was second top scorer in this season. Who was he?

38 At which ground did Everton play Queens Park Rangers in the FA Cup?

39 Who did Everton beat 2-0 in the quarter-finals of the FA Cup?

40 Everton drew the last match of the season to clinch the League title at Goodison. The score was 2-2, but who provided the opposition?

41 He scored Everton's first League goals, his only goals for the club, against Accrington. Who was he?

42 Who took over from Edgar Chadwick as Everton's top scorer in 1890?

43 And who was top scorer in 1892, unusual for a winger?

44 He was top League scorer in 1896 for the only time in a long and glorious Everton career?

45 Who scored Everton's first derby goal against Liverpool in 1894?

46 Where did Everton finish in the League which turned the new century, 1899/1900?

47 In season 1893/94 which Evertonian scored ten League goals in two games in a week?

48 In 1890/91 Fred Geary scored in the first six matches of the season. How many goals did he get in those matches?

49 And in 1889/90, the previous season, Geary scored fourteen goals in how many games?

50 Who were the first team to beat Everton in a League match?

51 What club record did Geary set in 1889/90 that he equalled the following season?

52 1892/93 was a bonanza year for goalkeepers. How many did Everton use in League matches?

53 With which team did Everton play a 5-5 draw in 1898?

54 Who was the club's top League scorer in 1902?

55 Who got into the history books by scoring six of Everton's seven goals in a League match against West Bromwich in 1893/94?

56 In their first League season, Everton scored 10 goals in a week (6-2, 4-2) against which team?

57 Name the two famous cousins who played in Everton's first League season?

58 In 1894 what was the score in the first League derby with Liverpool?

59 Who scored Everton's first League hat-trick against Derby County?

60 How did Everton start the 1894/95 League season in great style?

61 Who signed Bobby Collins from Celtic?

62 What first division club did Gordon Lee manage before Everton?

63 Who tragically died at Goodison in 1980 after a derby match with Liverpool?

64 Apart from Celtic what other Scottish club did Bobby Collins play for?

65 Which former Everton player scored the winning goal in the 1914 FA Cup final agaist Liverpool?

66 Which ex-Evertonian played with two different clubs under Bill Shankly?

67 He once played for Everton and won a European Cup medal in 1968 with another team. Who was he?

68 He was a winger, an England international, an England cricketer and later an Everton director. Who was he?

69 He captained Hearts at the age of 20, captained Everton in his only season at the club and died at the age of 31. Who was this fine player?

70 Who did Fred Geary play for after Everton?

71 Which former Everton player once coached Sparta Rotterdam?

72 What was strange about Walter Abbot's only England cap?

73 Which non-League side did Walter Balmer play for after leaving Everton?

74 Before he came to Everton this player was the last signing Stan Cullis made for Wolves. Who was he?

75 In 1909 Everton played Spurs twice in exhibition matches in which city?

76 What was Jock Dodds' first name?

77 Which Everton player was nicknamed Skippy?

78 Which old Evertonian signed for Preston but never played a game for them?

79 A former Everton player managed Wigan to Wembley success in 1985. Name him and the trophy they won?

80 During the First World War what unusual sport was staged at Goodison?

It was another great year for the Blues as they waltzed away with their second League title in five years. Everton went to the top of the first division in October and were never headed for the rest of the season. Packed with international stars, this team of the late twenties and early thirties was one of the greatest Everton ever had. See what you know about their glory run this season.

81 Once again Dixie Dean was Everton's top League scorer. How many goals did he notch up this time?

82 What goalscoring feat did Everton achieve in five matches in October?

83 In a season of scoring madness, who hit a hat-trick in the opening match at Goodison against Birmingham?

84 Who laid claim to the regular goalkeeping spot during the season and went on to become a great Everton hero?

85 And who was the keeper who lost his place to the new star?

86 Everton's title win spoiled a possible five consecutive titles which would have been a record even today. Which team lost out?

87 Who was second top scorer to Dean with 22 goals of his own?

88 During the season Dixie Dean hit two teams for five. Name the two unlucky clubs?

89 And which two clubs did Everton batter in nine against in League matches?

90 Name Everton's famous full-back partnership of the time?

91 And can you name the two flying wingers who provided the ammunition for the best strikers in the game?

92 Dixie Dean missed only two matches during the season. Who was the player who took his place and actually played his last two games for the club?

93 Even the Blues centre-half got five goals that season. Name him?

94 While Everton had a brilliant season in the League they lost out at the first hurdle in the FA Cup. Who beat the Blues 2-1 at Goodison?

95 And who scored Everton's only Cup goal of the season in that match?

96 What goalscoring record was set for the club during the season?

97 It's goals galore, but how many times did Everton players notch up hat-tricks or better during the season?

98 For all their efforts, two teams still beat Everton twice in the League campaign. Name either?

99 On Christmas Day 1931 Everton lost 3-5 to a team they beat 5-0 the very next day. Which team?

100 In the first six matches of the season, three Evertonians hit hat-tricks. Dixie Dean, Jimmy Dunn and who else?

101 Can you identify this famous Evertonian?

102 What was his first senior club?

103 In which year did he become Everton manager?

104 Against which team did he make his Everton debut?

105 From which club did Everton obtain the services of former captain Tom Booth?

106 Where did Dave Clements play his football before Goodison?

107 From which team did Everton buy Tony Kay?

108 Duncan McKenzie was Billy Bingham's last signing for the club. Name the year, the team he came from and the fee involved?

109 Who went to Nottingham Forest in 1970 as part of the deal which brought Henry Newton to Goodison?

110 To whom did Everton pay £120,000 for Graeme Sharp?

111 In 1978 Everton paid £300,000 for a 29-year-old player. Who was he and which club did he come from?

112 From which club did defender Warney Cresswell come in 1927?

113 Joe Donnachie had two spells with Everton, before and after the First World War. From which club did he come first time around?

114 From which team did enigmatic 30's winger Torry Gillick join Everton?

115 Name the year, the fee and the club he left when Bryan Hamilton joined Everton?

116 Dicky Downs, the acrobatic full-back, joined Everton in 1920 from which team?

117 From which team did Everton secure the services of goalkeeper Jim Arnold?

118 Half-back Willie Brown joined the club in 1914 from which Scottish team?

119 From where did Everton sign the great Jack Cock?

120 Pocket dynamo Wally Fielding was on which senior club's books as an amateur before joining Everton?

121 From which junior side did Everton sign Brian Harris?

122 Name the year, the fee and the team he left when Adrian Heath joined Everton?

123 From which team in Northern Ireland did Bobby Irvine join Everton in the twenties?

124 In June 1972 Everton paid a then British record fee for a goalkeeper. Who was he, and which team did he come from?

SOME CLUB FACTS

125 Who is the chairman of Everton Football Club?

126 What was the first ground Everton played at?

127 What is the worst defeat Everton have suffered?

128 What is the most League goals the club have scored in a season?

129 Who has been Everton's most capped player?

130 Who has made most League appearances for Everton?

131 Who were the club's first-ever opponents in 1879?

132 In which season did Everton first play in European competition?

133 What was the name of Everton's second ground?

134 Who were the first team Everton met in a Football League match?

135 What position did Everton attain in the first-ever Football League of 1888/89?

136 How many seasons have Everton spent in the second division?

137 Who is the club secretary?

138 What is Everton's record win?

139 In which year did Everton first win the League Championship?

140 In which year did the club first play at Goodison Park?

141 Who was the first manager of Everton?

142 Who were the club's first opponents in the FA Cup?

143 Who was the club's top goalscorer in their first season in the Football League of 1888/89?

144 In which year did Everton first win the FA Cup?

REMEMBER THIS SEASON—1938/39

In the last official season before the outbreak of the Second World War, Everton won the League Championship and would hold on to that title until 1947. Dixie Dean had departed from Goodison, but he left the club a goalscoring tradition that would be continued. Let's see what you know about that season.

145 Dixie Dean's prodigy finished top scorer that year. Who was he?

146 Which team did Everton hammer 8-0 in the fourth round of the FA Cup?

147 The only game Ted Sagar missed in goals, Everton lost 0-7. Who were they playing?

148 Who was the club's famous Welsh international centre-half of the time?

149 Which famous Evertonian bowed out with his one and only appearance of the season against Preston at Goodison in a goalless draw?

150 Who scored Everton's last official League goal for seven years?

151 Who was appointed manager of the club during the season?

152 Which Blues stalwart scored the only goal of his Everton career against Leicester?

153 Which team took Everton to a fifth round replay in the FA Cup before the Blues got through 2-1?

154 Against which team did Tommy Lawton get all four Everton goals in a 4-4 League draw?

155 Only one team beat the champions twice in the League, by 1-4 and 1-2, with Torry Gillick scoring in both matches. Who were the opponents?

156 Who was the tiny winger, who suffered from a physical handicap, who delighted Evertonians during the season with magnificent displays?

157 Who was the only player to appear in all of Everton's games?

158 Who finished second in the League to the new champions?

159 Veteran Jock Thomson played just over half of Everton's games at left-half before which player took over the position?

160 Who was the club's second top scorer of the season?

161 Who put the Blues out of the FA Cup in the sixth round by 0-2?

162 He grabbed a regular place in the team, missed only one match the whole season, scored a hat-trick against Sunderland, and went on to become a coach at Goodison when his career was over. Who?

Possibly one of the greatest Evertonians in history, a cruel injury put paid to Mark Higgins'
career.

163 Why was Everton's 59 points total significant?

164 Name the Scots winger who played five matches and later finished up beside Torry Gillick again in a Scottish club side?

165 Alex Young left Goodison to become player-manager of which team in Northern Ireland?

166 Which team did Mike Bernard join after leaving Everton in 1977?

167 Dixie Dean played only nine games for which English team when he left Goodison?

168 Who left Everton for West Bromwich in a straight swop for Andy King in 1982?

169 In 1977 Ronnie Goodlass was sold to a continental club. Which club was that?

170 Asa Hartford left Everton in 1981. Where did he go, and what fee did Everton receive for the player?

171 When Scottish international winger Alex Scott left Goodison he returned to his native land and which team?

172 Where did John Macconnachie go when he left Everton?

173 Goalkeeper Jimmy O'Neill left Everton to join which team?

174 After fifteen years at Goodison he left in 1978 to join Vancouver Whitecaps. Who was he?

175 Alf Milward played nine seasons with Everton before the turn of the century and then joined which team?

176 Name the club he went to and the fee received when Mike Pejic departed Everton?

177 Where did Jimmy Husband go when he left Everton?

178 When Ted Buckle left the club in 1955 where did he go?

179 Joe Harper departed after only fourteen months at Goodison. Where did he go, in what year, and what was the fee involved?

180 Popular winger Jackie Coulter joined which team when he left Everton?

181 Mick Lyons ended a wonderful association with Everton in 1982 to join which team?

182 Where did Billy Scott keep goal after he left Everton?

Gordon West, Monkeying around at Anfield.

183 Mickey Thomas had a short stay at Goodison before moving to which team, and what was the fee?

184 Where did Mike Trebilcock go when he left Everton?

185 In 1912 Everton lost six goals in a League match for the first time at Goodison. Who was the offending team?

186 When Everton won the title in 1915 who scored a hat-trick in the opening match of the season against Spurs?

187 Apart from Fred Geary who was the first Everton player to score 20 goals in a League season?

188 Between 1909 and 1911 Billy Scott saw off a challenge from which goalkeeper to keep his place in the team?

189 In 1908 who scored in ten consecutive League games for Everton?

190 Who played full-back for Everton from 1920-1927 in over 200 League matches and never scored a goal?

191 Who scored on his debut for Everton in a 1922 League game against Stoke and went on to become a famous goalscorer for the club?

192 Who beat Everton 2-5 in a League game in 1908 that was Jack Crelley's last game for the club?

193 When Everton won the 1915 title which team beat the Blues 1-5 in a League match?

194 Against which team did Billy Scott make his League debut for Everton?

195 When Everton first played the new Manchester United in the League in 1909 what was the score?

196 In what position did Tom Fleetwood make his League debut in 1911 against Bradford City?

197 Billy Scott's last League game for Everton was the last match of season 1911/12. Who provided the opposition at Goodison?

198 In 1919/20, the first season after World War I, where did Everton finish in the League?

199 Dixie Dean took over the regular centre-forward spot from which player?

200 When Everton started League football in 1919 after the war, their goalkeeper was the same as before hostilities started. Who was he?

201 In 1906 Everton beat another famous Lancashire team 9-1 in a League match at Goodison. Which team?

202 In 1909 Everton finished second in the League to which team?

203 In 1909 who became the first Everton player to score over 30 League goals in a season?

204 In 1920/21 who finished top League scorer for the club in his first season with Everton?

205 Can you identify this player?

206 Between May 1984 and May 1985 he captained Everton to four trophies. Name them?

207 Against which team did he make his Everton debut?

208 To which team was he once almost transferred?

209 Everton's first season in Europe was 1962/63, but in what Cup?

210 Who were Everton's first-ever European opponents?

211 What was the aggregate score in that tie?

212 In the 1963/64 European Cup, Everton lost to Inter Milan in the first round. What was the aggregate score?

213 What team did Everton beat to record their first European aggregate victory?

214 In 1965/66 who beat Everton in the Fairs Cup second round?

215 In the 1964/65 Fairs Cup which Scots team did Everton beat in the second round?

216 Name the goalkeeper who made his European debut against Valerengen in the 1964/65 Fairs Cup?

217 In the 1965/66 Fairs Cup which German team did Everton beat in the first round?

218 The first player to score for Everton in Europe was also scoring his only European goal. Who was he?

219 Which famous Evertonian made his first team debut in the San Siro Stadium in 1963?

220 What was the aggregate score when Everton beat Valerengen for their first win in a European tie?

221 In the 1964/65 Fairs Cup who beat Everton 2-3 on aggregate in the third round?

222 And which Everton player scored a goal in both legs of that game?

223 In the 1965/66 Fairs Cup, Everton drew 1-1 with Nuremburg in Germany in the first round first leg. Who scored Everton's goal?

224 Who was the first Everton player to score in a European away tie?

225 When Everton lost to Ujpest Doza in the 1965/66 Fairs Cup what was the score in the away leg?

226 In the 1966/67 Cup Winners Cup who made his European debut in the first round first leg and scored in the second leg?

227 And who did Everton beat in that tie?

228 Everton's left-back in their first-ever European match against Dunfermline was playing his only European tie for the club. Who was he?

REMEMBER THIS SEASON—1962/63

After almost quarter of a century the League Championship was Everton's once again. Harry Catterick had built a team in his short time as club manager that was invincible at Goodison and tenacious playing away from home. Everton also had their first taste of European football, if it could be called that, and went out at the first attempt. Indeed, Cup form seemed to go by the wayside as the Blues battled their way to a magnificent championship win.

229 Who was Everton's top scorer in their title winning run?

230 Which team finished second to Everton in the League after fighting a campaign almost right to the end?

231 Gordon West emerged as regular goalkeeper, taking over from which player?

232 And who took over as regular right-winger from Billy Bingham?

233 Who beat the Blues in the fifth round of the FA Cup by a single goal?

234 What was different about Johnny Morrissey when he played at Manchester City in a 1-1 draw in November 1962?

235 And who played his only game that season in that match and scored Everton's goal?

236 To whom did Brian Harris lose his regular place halfway through the season?

237 Everton of course qualified to play in the Charity Shield. Who were to be their opponents?

238 Which excellent club servant played wearing number 11 for only the last four matches of the season and scored one vital goal?

239 Johnny Morrissey hit a rare hat-trick in only his ninth game for the club in a League match at Goodison which the Blues won 4-2 against who?

240 Who were the first team to beat Everton in the League campaign?
241 Which team did the Blues beat 5-1 in the FA Cup fourth round?
242 Name the only two players who appeared in all championship matches?
243 How many teams won at Goodison during the season?
244 Everton's points total was a new club record. How many did they notch up on the glory run?
245 Everton lost 1-3 at Leicester in a League match in which Roy Vernon became the first Everton player to score for eight weeks. How was that possible in a championship-winning team?
246 Who scored his first Blues goal at Sheffield United as the team lost 1-2?
247 Who scored in the 1-0 League 'decider' match against Spurs at Goodison?
248 And who hit a hat-trick at Goodison against Fulham in the last League match as Everton celebrated their great championship win?

WHERE DID THEY COME FROM (2)

249 What was the record fee Everton paid Blackpool for Alan Ball?
250 From which team did John Connolly join Everton, and what was the fee?
251 From where did Everton secure the services of goalkeeper Tom Fern?
252 Winger Alan Irvine was an amateur until he joined Everton in 1981 from which team?
353 Teenager Jimmy Gabriel came to Goodison in 1960 from which Scottish club?
254 Winger Ted Critchley joined the club in 1926 from which team?
255 Where did Ray Wilson play before he came to Goodison?
256 In the fifties Everton went to Scotland for Jack Lindsay. What team did they get him from?

Scottish winger Alan Irvine, in his days at Goodison.

257 Tommy Johnson, the popular thirties forward, joined Everton from which team?

258 In 1927, Everton bought a young striker from Burnley who went on to become one of the greatest names in football. Who was he?

259 Can you name the year and the fee when Mike Pejic left Stoke for Everton?

260 Smart Arridge joined Everton in 1893 from which local team?

261 Mike Bernard came from Stoke City to Everton for what fee?

262 From where did Everton secure the signature of Irish winger Jackie Coulter?

263 Which team did Paul Bracewell leave for Goodison, and how much did Everton pay for his services?

264 When Bobby Collins arrived at Goodison for the second time, which Scottish club did he leave and what was the fee involved?

265 Everton signed him from Sunderland in 1920, and in his only full season with the club he finished top goalscorer. Who was he?

266 In 1921 Everton paid which Scottish club £4000 for half-back Hunter Hart?

267 Jimmy Dunn, one of Everton's most popular forwards ever, came to the club from which Scottish team?

268 Charlie Gee was another great Everton hero of the 30's. From which club did Everton sign the dynamic centre-half?

WHERE DID THEY GO (2)

269 Where did Jimmy Harris go when he left Everton in 1960?

270 When Billy Bingham's time as a player at Everton ended, which team did he join?

271 Ted Critchley, who paired up so often with Dixie Dean, left Everton in 1934. What team did he go to?

272 Captain of the 1915 League Championship winners, Jimmy Galt returned to Scotland after the First World War to play for which team?

273 Where did early hero Edgar Chadwick go when he left Everton?

274 Dave Hickson was one of the few players to have two spells with Everton. Which team did he join the first time he left, and what was the fee?

275 In which year did Fred Pickering leave Goodison, and who did he join?

276 Joe Royle's time at Goodison ended in which year, and which team did he go to?

277 When Brian Kidd left Everton after two years, which team did he join, in what year and what was the fee?

278 What was the year, the fee and the club involved when Steve McMahon left Everton?

279 Where did Jimmy Stein play after leaving Everton?

280 Name the forward who left Everton for Crystal Palace in 1972 for a fee of £100,000?

281 Where did Walter Abbott go when the stalwart wing-half left Goodison in 1908 after nine great years with Everton?

282 Which English team did Bobby Collins go to when he left Everton?

283 He was with Everton from 1910-1923 and played almost 300 times for the club in many positions before joining Oldham. Who was he?

284 When Andy Gray left Everton where did he go and what fee did the club receive for the brave striker?

285 In what year did John Hurst leave Everton, and where did he go?

286 When Joe Mercer left Everton, which team did he sign for and what was the fee?

287 With which club did Johnny Morrissey finish his career after leaving Everton?

288 Where did striker Jim Pearson go on leaving Goodison?

289 Who is this Everton player?
290 From which club did he join Everton?
291 What fee did Everton pay for his services?
292 What was his first Cup final appearance for Everton?

For the first time in 33 years Everton went to Wembley and won the FA Cup. The Blues had a marvellous Cup campaign with many exciting and memorable matches on the way to a thrilling final. League form belied the strength of the team, and progress was limited in the Fairs Cities Cup. However, the Cup triumph more than made up for any disappointment.

293 Where did Everton finish in the first division?

294 During the season the club used their first-ever League substitute. Who was he?

295 And who was the player he replaced?

296 How did Ray Wilson's season end with a little extra glory?

297 Which non-League team did the Blues beat 3-0 in the FA Cup fourth round?

298 When Everton beat Manchester United 1-0 in the FA Cup semi-final where was the match played?

299 Who scored Everton's goals in the FA Cup final against Sheffield Wednesday?

300 Against which team did Alex Young hit a League hat-trick in a 5-1 win for the Blues?

301 Who finished top League scorer during the season?

302 Who did Everton beat 3-0 in the fifth round of the FA Cup?

303 Apart from Gordon West, which other two keepers did the club use on first-team business during the season?

304 Who did Everton beat, again by 3-0, in the third round of the FA Cup?

305 Who won the League as Everton marched to Wembley?

306 Name at least five of the eight players who played in all Cup matches?

307 Who was Ray Wilson's full-back partner during the season?

308 Who were the scorers of Sheffield Wednesday's two Cup final goals?

309 Who took Everton to three games in the sixth round of the Cup?

310 Who scored the semi-final goal against Manchester United, one of only two goals he scored all season?

Martin Dobson, one-time favourite of the Everton fans.

311 Whose only two Cup appearances were the semi-final and the final?

312 And who was the unfortunate player who played every Cup tie except those two?

313 Who were Everton's first opponents in the FA Cup proper?

314 Everton's first Cup final was in 1893 when they lost 0-1 to which team?

315 And where was that final played?

316 Who was the first Everton player to score in an FA Cup final?

317 Who beat Everton 1-3 in the 1898 FA Cup semi-final at Molyneux?

318 In which year did Everton first meet Liverpool in the Cup and what was the outcome?

319 When Everton won the Cup for the first time in 1906 who did they beat in the final?

320 And which Everton player scored the only goal of that game?

321 Who were the first team to beat Everton in the Cup, by 0-6?

322 In 1886 Everton drew a team to be their first Cup opponents, but finished up losing to them 0-1 in a friendly because the Blues would have to have fielded inelegible players. Who were the team?

323 In 1889 Everton beat Derby 11-2 in the first round of the Cup. Name the three players who got hat-tricks for Everton in that match?

324 Which Everton player appeared in the finals of 1897, 1906 and 1907?

325 Everton lost the 1907 Cup final by 1-2 to which team?

326 And who scored Everton's goal in that final?

327 In 1895 and 1896 Everton lost to the same team in the same round of the Cup. Which team?

328 In 1906, who did Everton beat 2-0 in the semi-final at Villa Park?

329 In the 1905 semis Everton lost to Aston Villa by 1-2 after a 1-1 draw. Can you name either venue for these games?

330 In the 1893 semi-final Everton beat which team at the third attempt, the tie being played at Trent Bridge?

331 Which team beat Everton 2-3 in the 1897 Cup final?

332 And where was the 1897 final played?

333 Against which team did Dixie Dean score his first League goal for Everton?

334 In which season did Dixie Dean score his record 60 goals?

335 In 1928/29 what team took eleven goals off Everton in two League matches?

336 On Ted Sagar's League debut in 1930 Everton beat which team 4-0?

337 On Dixie Dean's debut Everton lost 1-3 to which team?

338 Who kept Ted Sagar out of the team in 1930/31?

339 The highest scoring derby match with Liverpool was at Anfield in 1933. What was the score?

340 How many goals did Dixie Dean hit in his first full season, 1925/26?

341 In December 1930 Everton beat Plymouth 9-1. Dean got four, but so did another player. Who was he?

342 When Tommy White finished top scorer in 1934 why was it such a remarkable feat?

343 In the season Dixie Dean got 60 League goals for Everton, which player got ten?

344 Who was the centre-half in the 1928 League-winning team?

345 In 1923 Dean had his second best scoring year with Everton. How many goals did he hit?

346 Who scored on his League debut in 1927 even though Everton lost 3-7 at Newcastle?

347 Name the Scottish winger who made his League debut in 1928 against Bolton as Dean hit another hat-trick?

348 Talking of the man's hat-tricks, against which team did he hit his first for Everton?

349 And against which team did Dean hit all five in 1927?

350 Everton won the 1928 title, but where did they finish in 1927 and 1929?

351 What happened to the club in 1930 for the first time in their history?

352 He was second top scorer when Everton won the 1932 League title, and was regular centre-half the following season. Who was he?

353 What career did Ray Wilson choose after football?

354 Which Everton player was a singer in the forties and made records?

355 This former Everton favourite was once reported killed in action during the First World War. Who was he?

356 Where was Alan Ball born?

357 With which club did Paul Bracewell play before Everton?

358 Everton are one of four teams to have won the second division and first division titles back to back. Name the other three?

359 Who was player/manager of Bury in 1984 after a career which took him to Goodison?

360 Who made his Everton debut when the Blues went to Old Trafford in 1956 and won 5-2 to end United's 26-game unbeaten run?

361 For which American team did Gary Jones play?

362 In 1972 Everton played a Great Britain Select in a benefit match for whom?

363 What did Dixie Dean prefer to be called?

364 Who sold Howard Kendall as a player from Everton?

365 Who was manager of Stoke when Howard Kendall was appointed coach of that club?

366 Which former Everton player was a director of Manchester United for fifty years?

367 John Bell played for two Scottish clubs, Dumbarton and who?

368 In 1977 Everton loaned two players to Queens Park Rangers. Mike Buckley and who else?

369 Who signed for Everton leaning out of a train window in Dublin?

370 How was Jimmy Cunliffe better known?

371 Where was Gary Stevens born?

372 At what age did Joe Royle make his Everton debut in 1966?

Mike Walsh, always a favourite at Goodison.

373 Who is this exciting player?

374 In which year did he join Everton?

375 Against which country did he make his England debut?

376 Against which team did he make his Everton debut?

After an exciting season, Everton emerged as clear winners of the first division title for the seventh time in their history. In a storming finish the club had a record undefeated run, with some classic performances to capture the honour. See what you remember about it.

377 Who was Everton's top League scorer with 23 goals?

378 By what points margin did the Blues win the title?

379 What new club points record was set during the season?

380 Struggling uncharacteristically, the Blues managed a 1-0 win in the second round of the League Cup against which team?

381 Name the two players who were in the title-winning sides of 1963 and 1970?

382 Who were the only opponents to score three goals at Goodison during the season?

383 Who beat Everton 0-2 in the League Cup fourth round?

384 Tommy Wright scored a rare goal, his only one of the season, to give Everton a vital 1-0 win in a League match at home against which team?

385 Everton's second top scorer played only 15 games. Who was he?

386 Which team were runners-up to Everton in the League?

387 Which four Evertonians played in the World Cup finals in Mexico at the end of the season?

388 Who was Everton's regular left-back during the season?

389 Who beat Everton 1-2 in the third round of the FA Cup?

390 Which full-back made his Everton debut in December 1969 in a League match at Goodison against Derby?

391 In the third round of the League Cup who did Everton beat 1-0 after a 0-0 draw?

392 Alan Whittle replaced which player as the regular number seven at the latter end of the season?

393 Everton had their best winning run in the League for almost 40 years. How many consecutive games did they win, and how many did they actually go undefeated?

394 Who covered the centre-half position in the last few matches in place of Brian Labone?

A head above them all is former Blues striker Mike Ferguson.

395 Who scored in his first outing of the season for the fourth consecutive year?

396 Everton only scored three times in five cup matches. Name the two players who got the goals?

397 From which team did Everton sign Imre Varadi?

398 Frank Jefferis was a big favourite at Goodison before the First World War. Where did he come from?

399 The first time Andy King joined Everton, which team did he come from?

400 John Macconnachie was a stalwart defender around the First World War. What Scottish team did Everton sign him from?

401 Name the year, the fee and the team he left when Peter Reid came to Everton?

402 From which team did Everton sign Walter Abbott in 1899?

403 Where did Alan Biley play before he joined up with Everton?

404 When Cliff Britton commenced his association with Everton in 1930, which club did he come from?

405 Who went from St Johnstone to Everton in 1938 only to return to his native Scotland the same year after just five games with Everton?

406 Apart from Sheffield Wednesday, name two other senior teams Dave Clements played for before coming to Everton?

407 Asa Hartford played a mere three games for which team before he came to Everton?

408 From which non-League club did Everton sign Jimmy Cunliffe in 1930?

409 Joe Donnachie returned to Everton in 1919. Which Scottish club did he leave to come back to Goodison?

410 In 1979 Everton paid a then club record £650,000 to Aston Villa for which player?

411 When Joe Harper came south from Aberdeen in 1972 Everton paid the Scottish club an incoming record fee for the player. What was the fee?

412 Another Scottish favourite at Goodison was winger Jimmy Stein. From which Scottish team did he come?

413 Tommy G. Jones was on Everton's books for fourteen years after coming to Goodison from which team?

414 Everton paid £350,000 in 1974 for a striker. Who was he and where did he come from?

415 From which team did Everton sign Ian Atkin?

416 Sam Chedgzoy played for which local side before joining Everton?

BLUES IN THE FA CUP—AROUND TWO WARS

417 Name the Everton team which won the FA Cup in 1906?

418 In 1912 Everton beat Bury 6-0 in a replay after a 1-1 draw, with

Martin Dobson finds the net against Cambridge.

both games played at Goodison. Who got four of Everton's six in the replay?

419 What non-League team did Everton beat 3-1 in the third round of the Cup in 1927?

420 Who did Everton beat 9-1 in the sixth round of the 1931 FA Cup?

421 In 1931 Everton reached the semi-final before losing to which team?

422 Who beat Everton 0-3 in a replayed semi-final at Old Trafford in the 1910 FA Cup?

423 In 1914 Everton lost 1-2 to a team in their second last season as a League side in the first round of the Cup. Which team beat them?

424 In 1922 Everton lost 0-6 at Goodison to a second division team who had only been elected to the Football League the previous year. Name the team?

425 In 1931 Dixie Dean got four goals in both the fourth and sixth round matches. Name the teams on the receiving end?

426 Dixie Dean scored on his FA Cup debut in 1926 to give Everton a 1-1 draw, but they lost the replay by 0-1. Who were the opponents?

427 When Everton set out in defence of the Cup in 1934 they lost at the first hurdle by 0-3 to which team?

428 In 1935 who scored six goals in his first five FA Cup ties for Everton?

429 In 1915 which London club beat Everton 0-2 in the semi-final at Villa Park?

430 Everton also lost their first FA Cup tie after the First World War, by 0-2 in 1920. Which team beat the Blues?

431 When Everton won the 1933 Cup who did they beat 2-1 in the semi-final and where?

432 Who were Everton's opponents when the club won the Cup for the first time at Wembley in 1933?

433 Who were Everton's three scorers in that historic match?

434 What colour of shirts did Everton wear in the 1933 final?

435 And what was the new addition to the shirts?

436 Who captained the 1933 FA Cup-winning team?

THE LEAGUE CAMPAIGNS—THIRTIES TO FIFTIES

437 In 1934/35 Everton lost 0-7 in the League but a month later beat the same team 6-4 in the FA Cup. Which team?

438 When Tommy Lawton scored on his debut at Wolves in 1937, Everton were heavily beaten. What was the score?

439 He played only half of season 1946/47 but finished Everton's top scorer. Who was he?

440 Which team once beat Everton 1-11 in a wartime League match?

441 How many times was Dixie Dean top League scorer for Everton?

442 Apart from Ted Sagar, the last pre-war player to leave the team was in 1950. Who was he?

443 In 1954 when Everton were promoted back to the first division who won the second division title on goal average from the Blues?

444 Name the young striker who made his debut in 1956/57 against Newcastle at Goodison and served the club for ten years?

445 When Everton were relegated in 1951 they had their lowest points total for 55 years. How many points did they have?

446 In 1948/49 Everton set an unenviable club scoring record in the League. What was it?

447 Dixie Dean's last goal was in the first match of 1937/38 season, in which the Blues lost 1-4 at Goodison to which team?

448 Name the right-winger who made his Everton debut in a League match in December 1935 and scored nine times before the end of the season?

449 Where did the club finish in the first League championship after the war, 1946/47?

450 In 1948 who scored a double on his debut as Everton beat Huddersfield by 2-0 in a League match?

451 In 1956 Jimmy O'Neill lost the goalkeeper's job to who?

452 And who did Jimmy O'Neill replace around 1951 as regular keeper?

453 In 1955/56 who finished top scorer in his first season at Goodison?

454 In 1952/53 Everton nearly became a third division team. Where did they finish in the second division?

455 Who made his Everton League debut first, Brian or Jimmy Harris?

456 In 1951 Everton lost 0-6 in their last game to go down to the second division. Who were the opposition?

457 Name this outstanding player?
458 From which team did he join Everton?
459 What fee did Everton pay for him?
460 From whom did he take over in the first team?

Funny asking questions about a season in which the club won nothing, but there were many important points in this one. A change of manager at the halfway stage, an epic League Cup final, an appearance in the FA Cup semi-final and more made this season one of the great talking points in the club's history. See what you remember.

461 What was the managerial change during the season?

462 Where did the Blues eventually finish in the League?

463 In the League Cup fourth round an Andy King double helped Everton to a 3-0 win over which team?

464 And in the fifth round another Andy King double helped Everton to a 3-0 win over which team?

465 Which team did Everton play four times during the season without winning once?

466 In the League Cup final matches, three different players wore the number two for Everton. Name them?

467 Who was Gordon Lee's first major signing for the club?

468 Who was the club's top goalscorer during the season?

469 In the first replay of the League Cup final against Aston Villa, who scored to give Everton a 1-1 draw?

470 And who scored an own goal in that match to even the scores?

471 In a hectic season, only one player managed to appear in all 58 matches. Name him?

472 Who took Everton to a replay in the FA Cup fourth round?

473 Who was the first major signing Billy Bingham made for Everton?

474 In the first game of the FA Cup semi-final against Liverpool, who were Everton's scorers in the 2-2 draw?

475 Name the three keepers who were used in the first team during the season?

476 Who did Everton beat 2-1 on aggregate in the League Cup semi-final?

477 What was the score in the second replay of the League Cup final against Villa?

478 And name the players who scored for Villa in that match?

479 Who did Everton beat 2-0 with goals from Latchford and Pearson in the FA Cup quarter-finals?

480 Who were Everton's scorers in the second replay of the League Cup final at Maine Road against Villa?

481 Which two senior clubs did Wally Boyes play for when he left Everton?

482 Stalwart Brian Harris left Goodison in the twilight of his career to join which team?

483 He was with Everton for five seasons during the seventies and then returned to the club he had come from for £100,000 in 1979. Who was he?

484 Which team did winger Albert Geldard join for £5000 in 1938?

485 Where did Jack Cock go when he left Everton in 1925?

486 When goalkeeper Albert Dunlop left Goodison in 1963 which team did he go to?

487 Which club manager bought Alan Irvine from Everton?

488 Eric Moore left Goodison for which club, and what was the fee?

489 Where did Keith Newton go when his time came to leave Everton?

490 When Charlie Parry, the famous nineteenth century defender, left Everton, which team snapped him up?

491 Who signed goalkeeper Andy Rankin from Everton?

492 Trevor Ross went abroad after leaving Goodison. Which team did he join?

493 In which year did Dennis Stevens leave Everton, and what team did he join?

494 Where did Ray Wilson go after his great service to Everton?

495 George Telfer joined an American team when he made his exit from Goodison. Which one?

496 When Alan Ball was transferred from Everton in 1971 it was for a record fee. What was the fee and which club paid it?

497 Where did goalkeeper Billy Coggins go when he left Everton?

498 Which Everton goalkeeper left the club for Port Vale in 1924 after eleven years at Goodison?

499 Who signed John Gidman for Manchester United when that club bought him from Everton in 1981?

500 In which year did Tommy Lawton leave Goodison, which club did he join, and what fee did they pay for him?

MISCELLANEOUS (3)

501 Who signed Howard Kendall for Everton?

502 Which former Everton player was Ron Atkinson's first signing for Manchester United?

503 Who in 1984 turned out for a village team called Everton?

504 Name the manager who took Andy King from Everton to QPR.

505 At which club did Alan Ball start his managerial career?

506 In 1952 which former Everton player was given the unusual position of coach to Peru?

507 Which former Everton player once pioneered coaching in New York?

508 Which trophy did Mike Bernard help Stoke to win in 1972, their first success in 108 years?

509 Who was the only ever-present in the team which won the 1985 League championship?

510 Name the cousins who were at Goodison in 1951, one playing regularly and the other making a name for himself later?

511 Which former Everton player made a career for himself as a Football Development Officer on Merseyside?

512 Where was Edgar Chadwick born?

513 Who was appointed manager of Northern Ireland while still an Everton player?

514 Jock Dodds was once given a free transfer as a teenager. Which team missed the boat?

515 What was Torry Gillick's proper first name?

516 How old was Adrian Heath when Howard Kendall paid a record £700,000 for his services?

517 Tommy E. Jones left Everton and later became a coach of Montreal. In which country?

Adrian Heath in determined mood.

518 Where was Cliff Britton manager before Everton?
519 Which former Everton player once appeared in goal for New Brighton in a Football League match at the age of 52?
520 Which former Everton player once was capped for Scotland while playing reserve football?

THE LEAGUE CAMPAIGNS—INTO THE SIXTIES

521 When Everton won the 1963 title, name the teams who beat them at Goodison?
522 Who was the club's top League scorer in 1959/60 season?
523 When defending the title in 1963/64 where did Everton finally finish in the League?
524 In 1966/67 which youngster played four games near the end of the season and scored three goals?

525 Name the Scottish international winger who played briefly for Everton in 1960?

526 When Everton lost 4-10 to Spurs in 1958, which Everton player hit a consolation hat-trick?

527 Who was the club's top scorer in 1963/64 season?

528 In 1964/65 Fred Pickering missed only one game, a 1-1 draw at home to West Ham. Who played centre-forward in his place?

529 Who scored on his League debut for Everton in the first game of 1966/67 in a 1-0 win at Fulham?

530 Name the Irish hero who made his debut for the club at Fulham in a 3-2 win in 1960?

531 In 1953 Everton lost eight goals in a second division match after having beaten the same team 2-1 the previous day. Which team was that?

532 Who played the last nine matches of 1963/64 season and scored nine goals?

533 Name the young defender who made a quiet debut at Blackpool in a 1-1 draw in 1964?

534 In Alex Young's League debut for Everton in December 1960 which team beat Everton 1-3 at Goodison?

535 In 1964 Everton won 4-0 to record their first League win for 13 years at which ground?

536 In 1962 Everton scored eight goals in a first division match for the first time in 30 years. Who got blasted?

537 In 1959 Everton lost 2-8 in a League match to which team?

538 He made his League debut at Goodison in 1962 as Everton beat Wolves 4-0. Who was he?

539 In 1965 who scored his first goal for the club after 248 League games, and who were the opposition?

540 In 1958 Brian Labone was on the losing side on his Everton debut. Who spoiled the occasion by winning 1-2 at their own patch?

Joe Royle in combat with Jimmy Rimmer in 1969.

541 Who is this Everton player?

542 From which club did he join Everton?

543 Against which country did he win his first England cap?

544 In which year did he join Everton?

545 In the 1966/67 Cup Winners Cup who beat Everton in the second round?

546 Who scored Everton's first European hat-trick?

547 Who was the first substitute used by Everton in a European tie?

548 In the 1970/71 European Cup who did Everton beat on penalties in the second round?

549 In the third round of the 1970/71 European Cup the club went out in the third round on away goals to which team?

550 In the 1975/76 UEFA Cup, Everton lost in the first round to AC Milan. What was the aggregate score?

551 In the 1978/79 UEFA Cup who did Everton beat 10-0 on aggregate in the first round?

552 And what was the score in each leg of that tie?

553 In the 1978/79 UEFA Cup, Everton went out on away goals again, this time in the second round to which team?

554 Name the young Scot whose only European tie for Everton was at Goodison in the 1979/80 UEFA Cup against Feyenoord wearing number seven?

555 Dave Clements' only European appearance for the club was as a substitute against which team?

556 In the 1966/67 Cup Winners Cup when Everton went out to Real Zaragoza, who scored in the Blues' 1-0 win in the Goodison leg?

557 In the 1970/71 European Cup, Everton beat Keflavik 6-2 in the first round first leg. Who were Everton's scorers?

558 And when they won 3-0 in the second leg of that tie, who were the scorers?

559 When Everton went out to Panathanaikos in the 1970/71 European Cup, who scored for the Blues in the 1-1 draw at Goodison after coming on as a substitute?

560 What was the last European tie Gordon West played in?

561 When AC Milan put Everton out of the 1975/76 UEFA Cup the Blues used a different keeper in each leg, and for both it was their only European game for the club. Can you name them?

562 Who were the Blues scorers when Everton beat Dukla Prague 2-1 at home in the second round first leg of the 1978/79 UEFA Cup?

563 In the 1979/80 UEFA Cup who beat Everton 0-2 on aggregate in the first round?

564 Which two players share the most European appearances for Everton?

REMEMBER THIS SEASON 1977/78

This was an important season for the club, even though they failed to win a trophy. It was Gordon Lee's first full season in charge, and his team were finding the net regularly and managed a respectable finish in the League.

See what you can remember about the season.

565 Where did Everton finish in the League?

566 Everton finished as highest scoring team in the first division. How many goals did they score?

567 Who did Everton beat by 4-1 in the third round of the FA Cup?

568 Who came in as regular goalkeeper at the start of the season?

569 Who did Everton beat 3-1 in the third round of the League Cup?

570 Whose last game for Everton was in a 4-4 draw with Newcastle at Goodison?

571 Who was the club's top scorer during the season?

572 Signed at the start of the season he made the number 11 jersey his property. Who?

573 Against which team did Bob Latchford hit four out of five goals in a League match?

574 Who was the second top scorer for the club?

575 In the third round of the League Cup the Blues drew 2-2 at Goodison and won the replay away from home by 2-1. Who were their opponents?

576 Who was bought from Arsenal halfway through the season to fill the number six jersey?

577 Name the three players who appeared in all matches during the season?

578 Who beat the Blues 1-4 in the fifth round of the League Cup?

579 And who scored Everton's goal in that match?

580 Who took over as regular centre-half at the beginning of the season?

581 In the fourth round of the FA Cup Everton lost 2-3 to which team?

582 Name the young defender who made his debut as a substitute for George Telfer in a League match against Leicester at Goodison?

583 Which team scored six in a League match at Goodison?

584 How many Everton players got on the scoresheet in League matches?

WHERE DID THEY COME FROM (4)

585 In which year and from which club did Mike Trebilcock join Everton?

586 19th century Everton hero Bob Kelso had two spells with Everton. From which club did he join the second time around?

587 From which team did the Blues sign popular twenties wing-half Neil McBain?

588 Alex Parker was another in the long line of Scots to cross the Border to Goodison. What Scottish team did he play for?

589 Who cost Everton a British record £300,000 fee in 1974?

590 Val Harris came from Ireland to Goodison in 1907. Which Irish team did he play for?

591 Name Peter Eastoe's three senior clubs before he joined Everton?

592 He captained the 1915 League Championship-winning team in his only season at Goodison after joining from Glasgow Rangers. Who was he?

593 Name Andy Gray's three senior teams before Everton?

594 From which club did John Bailey join Everton?

595 Jack Crelley was born in Liverpool but ended up at Goodison via which team in 1899?

A young and pensive Kevin Richardson.

596 From where did Everton sign tiny winger Wally Boyes?
597 For which Irish team did Tom Clinton play before coming to Everton?
598 Another pair in Everton's Irish connection came to the club in a joint deal in 1946 from Shamrock Rovers. Name them?
599 From which team did Everton sign Albert Geldard?
600 Harold Hardman, the famous little winger who graced Goodison just after the turn of the century, came from which team?
601 Name the year, the fee and the club he left when Brian Kidd became an Evertonian?
602 In 1963 Everton paid £46,000 for which Scotland winger?
603 Tom Fleetwood came to Everton in 1911 from which team?
604 In which year, and from which team, did Stan Bentham join Everton?

WHERE DID THEY GO (4)

605 Where did Irish internationalist Bobby Irvine go when he was transferred from Everton?
606 In which year and what was the fee when Ken McNaught joined Aston Villa from Everton?
607 Which team did Alex Parker go to when he left Everton?
608 Neil Robinson left Everton to join which club?
609 Name the team who bought Henry Newton from Everton, the year and the fee involved?
610 Where did the versatile Mick Meagan go when he left Everton?
611 Gary Jones was transferred from Goodison in 1976 to which team, and what fee did they pay for him?
612 After two years at Goodison, the enigmatic Duncan McKenzie took his services to which team?
613 Who did George Brewster play for after his time at Everton?
614 Terry Darracott was another player who tried American soccer after he left Everton, but can you name the team he went to?
615 Jimmy Dunn went south after he left Everton. How far south?
616 In which year did Bryan Hamilton leave Everton for Millwall?

617 Where did Mick Buckley go when he left Goodison?

618 Can you name the year, the fee and the club involved when Derek Temple was transferred from Everton?

619 Sandy Young, such a prolific goalscorer before the First World War, joined which London team when he left Everton?

620 Name the goalkeeper who left Everton to go to Luton in 1978?

621 Which club bought John Connolly from Everton?

622 In which year did Jimmy Gabriel leave Goodison, and what team did he join?

623 Name the Everton centre-forward who became one of the first players to move across Stanley Park to Anfield way back in 1894?

624 Colin Todd's Everton career lasted one short year before he was transferred to which team, and how much did Everton receive for the player?

625 No problem here. Name the player?
626 For which Irish club did he once play?
627 For how many years was he an Everton player?
628 How did he once fracture his skull?

629 In 1939 Everton played their last FA Cup tie for seven years, going out in the sixth round to which team?

630 Who scored Everton's last goal in the FA Cup before the war?

631 In 1946 Everton lost 1-2 to Preston in the FA Cup but played them again. Why?

632 In 1962, which non-League team did Everton beat 4-0 in the third round, and which player got a double for Everton in his FA Cup debut for the club?

633 In the 1946 Cup when Everton lost 1-2 to Preston, who scored his first Cup goal for Everton in that match?

634 Who beat Everton 3-4 in the 1953 Cup semi-final?

635 What Cup hoodoo hung over Everton in the fifties?

636 In 1960 Everton lost at the first Cup hurdle to a third division team. Who were they?

637 In 1935, Everton won a classic fourth round Cup replay by 6-4 against which team?

638 In the 1965 FA Cup, Everton drew 2-2 at Goodison in the third round and won the replay 3-0 away from home. Who were the opposition?

639 In the 1959 Cup campaign, who scored five times in four games for Everton?

640 In the 1953 Cup semi-final against Bolton, who scored a double for Everton as they went down 3-4?

641 When the Blues won the Cup in 1966 how many goals did they lose in the seven matches before the final?

642 Everton lost 0-2 to Liverpool in the 1950 semi-final at Maine Road. Which two famous football characters got Liverpool's goals?

643 In the 1937 Cup, Everton beat Bournemouth 5-0 in the third round with an Irish international getting two and a Scot also scoring two. Both players also had spells with the same Scottish club. Who were they?

644 Who beat Everton 0-4 at Goodison in the fourth round of the 1955 Cup?

645 In the 1965 Cup, Everton went out in the fourth round but

played four matches because of replays. Who scored for Everton in every match?

646 In 1937 Spurs beat Everton 3-4 in a classic fifth round replay. Dixie Dean got two for Everton, but who got the other on his Cup debut for Everton?

647 Who came to Goodison in 1965 for a replay and beat Everton 1-2?

648 When Everton won the 1966 Cup, who scored in every round except the semi-final?

REMEMBER THIS SEASON 1983/84

Everton won the FA Cup for the first time in 18 years. It was a magnificent achievement and gave Howard Kendall his first trophy as manager of the club he had graced for so long as a player. Everton also appeared in the League Cup final, and had a creditable year in the League. Unfold the season through the questions.

649 Everton's FA Cup fourth round tie took three games before the Blues despatched which opponents?

650 Why was eleven goals significant and depressing at the New Year stage of the season?

651 Who was the club's top scorer during the season?

652 Where did Everton finish in the League?

653 Who did Everton beat 2-1 in the FA Cup quarter-finals and name the two players who scored the goals?

654 Who did Everton beat 1-0 in the FA Cup semi-final, where was the match played and who scored Everton's goal?

655 Who were the two scorers for Everton in the FA Cup final?

656 Name the Everton Cup-winning team?

657 Who scored Liverpool's goal in the League Cup final replay which beat Everton?

658 Who did Everton beat 4-1 in the League Cup quarter-finals after a 1-1 draw?

659 Who did the Blues beat 2-1 on aggregate in the League Cup semi-final?

660 His last goal for Everton came in a League match in which Everton beat Watford for only their second home win of the season. Who was he?

661 In his only game of the season he scored at Goodison in a 1-1 draw with Manchester United and was substituted by a youngster making his first-team debut. Name both players?

662 Andy Gray's League debut at Goodison was against which team?

663 And his first goal was at Goodison in a 1-1 draw with which team?

664 Who did Derek Mountfield replace as centre-half?

665 Who played in every cup match except the FA Cup semi and final and the replay of the League Cup final?

666 Who wore the number 11 jersey in the League Cup final replay against Liverpool?

667 Who was the substitute in the League Cup final replay who came on for Alan Irvine?

668 What was Mark Higgins' last game for Everton?

THE LEAGUE CAMPAIGNS—INTO THE SEVENTIES

669 In 1966/67 who finished top League scorer in his first season with the club?

670 In 1967/68 Alan Ball hit four out of six for Everton in a League match at which ground?

671 In 1967/68 who appeared 13 times as a substitute in League games for Everton?

672 Who took over as regular goalkeeper at the start of the 1972/73 season?

673 In 1975/76 season what did Martin Dobson and Mike Lyons do that no outfield player at the club had done since 1970?

674 Joe Royle's first League hat-trick came in 1968 as Everton beat which team 7-1 at Goodison?

675 Name the only two outfield players who appeared in all matches in the Championship-winning team of 1970?

676 In 1971/72 Everton scored their lowest total of League goals since their first-ever season. How many did they score?

Young Joe McBride, who had a short but exciting Everton career.

677 In season 1973/74 two players wore six different jerseys during the season. Can you name them?

678 In 1972/73 in a bid to solve the chronic lack of goals Everton used six players in the number nine jersey. How many can you name?

679 In 1977/78 who beat Everton 2-6 in a League game at Goodison?

680 In 1968 Gordon West missed his only League match in three years in a 1-1 draw at West Ham. Who was in goal in that match?

681 Where did Everton finish in the League in 1977/78 season?

682 In 1972/73 who were joint-top League scorers with seven goals each, and there were three of them?

683 In the game Gordon West missed at West Ham in 1968, which player made his last League appearance for Everton?

684 In the low-scoring 1971/72 season, eight of Everton's meagre total came in one match against which team?

685 In 1974/75 Everton went 15 games undefeated in the League then lost by 2-3 to a team in the first division for one season. Who were they?

686 In 1970/71 which two players wore the number three shirt for most of the season?

687 Where did Dai Davies make his League debut for Everton in 1974?

688 When Bob Latchford finished top scorer in 1974/75 with 17 League goals, why was it so significant?

MISCELLANEOUS (4)

689 Who at Everton was nicknamed Chico?

690 In which country was Pat Van den Hawe born?

691 Who became coach of Everton after Cliff Britton left?

692 Where was Howard Kendall's first coaching job?

693 Where was Welsh internationalist Smart Arridge born?

694 Who was Everton's Little General?

695 Who joined Everton from Wigan in 1933 with Stan Bentham?

696 What was Edgar Chadwick's trade?

697 How did Sam Chedgzoy help to change the rules of football in 1924?

698 Who was made captain of Everton after Peter Farrell?

699 What was Peter Eastoe's first senior club?

700 What was Wally Fielding's first name?

701 Who was the manager who brought Joe Harper to Everton?

702 Name the 14-year-old England schoolboy international sensation Everton signed in 1962?

703 When Bob Latchford hit 30 League goals in 1977/78 what was his special reward?

704 Who won a Scottish League-winners medal in 1913 and an English one with Everton in 1915?

705 Where was Ted Buckle born?

706 Name the two clubs Warney Cresswell managed on retirement from playing?

707 In which county was Jack Cock born?

708 Which Everton player was once a violinist with the Halle Orchestra?

PICTURE QUIZ (8)

709 Who's this former Everton stalwart?
710 In how many games did he wear Everton's colours?
711 How many England caps did he win?
712 In which year did he retire from football?

The first 17 questions here concern the Everton team which won the 1985 Cup Winners Cup.

713 Name Everton's Cup-winning team.

714 Who did Everton beat 3-1 in the final?

715 Where was the final played?

716 Who were Everton's scorers in the final?

717 And who scored for the opposition?

718 Who scored the goal which took Everton through the first round on a 1-0 aggregate against University College, Dublin?

719 Who did Everton beat in the second round of the Cup?

720 In the second round Everton won 1-0 away from home in the first leg. Who scored for the club in that match?

721 And who were the scorers in the 3-0 second leg at Goodison?

722 From which country did their second round opponents come?

723 In the third round whose hat-trick gave Everton a 3-0 win at Goodison in the first leg against Fortuna Sittard?

724 And who were the two scorers in the 2-0 second leg win?

725 In that second leg tie with Sittard, who came on as a substitute for Kevin Ratcliffe to make his only European appearance?

726 What was the score in the first leg of the semi-final against Bayern Munich?

727 Name the scorers in the semi-final second leg at Goodison when Everton beat Bayern Munich 3-1?

728 Who made his European debut against Fortuna Sittard and played in all the other ties?

729 And who was the captain who lifted the coveted trophy?

730 Who has been Everton's top scorer in Europe?

731 Apart from Dunfermline, what is the only other Scottish team Everton have met in Europe?

732 Who were the last team to win at Goodison against Everton in a European match?

The 1985 Champions with the Canon League trophy.

In their greatest-ever season, the club won the League championship and the European Cup Winners Cup, and reached Wembley again for the FA Cup final. Howard Kendall's efforts had shown fruit in a spectacular fashion, putting Everton to the forefront of world football. Revel in these questions.

733 By how many points did Everton win the League?

734 Who played in only three full League games and scored in two?

735 Who was top League scorer for the club?

736 Who did Everton beat 1-0 in the FA Cup quarter-finals after a 2-2 draw at Goodison?

737 Who beat Everton in a shocker in the League Cup fourth round?

738 Which non-League team visited Goodison in the FA Cup fifth round?

739 Pat Van den Hawe took over the number three spot from whom?

740 Who did Everton beat 4-0 in the League to go top, where they stayed for the rest of the season?

741 Name the young Scot who wore number 11 for the Blues in the last game of the League season at Luton?

742 In the Cup Winners Cup first round Everton beat UCD. Who are UCD?

743 Who scored most Cup Winners Cup goals for Everton?

744 Who did Everton beat 2-1 in the FA Cup semi-final?

745 What was Everton's new points record in the League?

746 What club League record was equalled after 54 years?

747 Who scored the FA Cup final goal for Manchester United which cost Everton the Cup?

748 Everton lost twice in the League at Goodison, conceding four goals each time. Who were the winning teams?

749 Paul Wilkinson's first goal for Everton gave them a 1-0 win over which team at Goodison?

750 Why was the Cup final win sweet revenge for Manchester United?

751 Who made his Everton debut at the start of the season at Wembley?

752 Who did Everton beat 2-0 at Goodison to clinch the League title?

753 In which year and from which team did Trevor Ross join Everton?

754 Bobby Parker was a prolific goalscorer for Everton from 1913-1921. From which team did he join Everton?

755 From where did the Blues secure the services of Keith Newton?

756 In which year and what was the fee involved when Johnny Morrissey crossed Stanley Park to join Everton?

757 Cyril Lello came to Everton in the forties from which team?

758 When Andy King came to Everton for the second time, which club did he come from?

759 From which team did Everton sign Norman Greenhalgh?

760 Fred Geary, who had an eye for goals before the turn of the century, left which club to come to Everton?

Pat Van den Hauwe rides a tackle from former Evertonian Kevin Langley.

761 In which year did Bertie Freeman join Everton from Arsenal?

762 Name the three League clubs Jock Dodds played for before Everton?

763 Full-back Billy Cook came south from Scotland in 1932 from which team to join up at Goodison?

764 From where did Everton procure the signature of goalkeeper Billy Coggins?

765 In which year did Joe Clennell sign for the Blues from Blackburn Rovers?

766 Winger John Bell left the Scottish champions in 1892 to join Everton. Which team was that?

767 Which two League teams did Billy Bingham play for before Everton?

768 Sandy Brown came down from Scotland and had eight good years at Goodison. Where did he come from?

769 From which team did Everton sign Edgar Chadwick in 1888?

770 Another Scot who captained Everton came from the same team in the same year as John Bell, 1892. He was a half-back, but can you name him?

771 In which year and from which team did Ted Buckle join Everton?

772 George Brewster was yet another northern light from Scotland. What team did he sign from?

THE LEAGUE CAMPAIGNS—TO THE PRESENT

773 In season 1978/79, Everton broke which club record in a cracking start?

774 In 1977/78 what did Bob Latchford achieve that no Everton player since Dixie Dean had done?

775 In 1980/81 who was Everton's first-team keeper for one season?

776 In 1979/80 which of the following players was first to make his League debut for the club; Joe McBride, Kevin Ratcliffe, or Gary Megson?

777 In 1979/80 when the club were fighting to stay in the first division the team beat Southampton 2-0 in April. Which two players got their first goal for the club in that match?

778 Who took over as regular centre-half in 1978/79?

779 When Mark Higgins made his League debut in 1976 at Sunderland in what position did he play?

780 Neville Southall lost his Everton place after which League match in 1982?

781 Against which team did Derek Mountfield make his Everton debut?

782 Against which team did Neville Southall make his League debut for Everton in 1981?

783 Who were the only team to beat Everton in the 1978 half of season of 1978/79?

784 Who was the club's top League scorer in 1978/79?

David Johnson, who crossed Stanley Park, seen here putting the pressure on John Wile.

785 Why was Bob Latchford's four goals in a League match against Queens Park Rangers in 1977 so special?

786 Against which team did Colin Todd score his only League goal for the club in 1978/79 season?

787 Who was the club's top League scorer in season 1980/81?

788 Bob Latchford scored his last goal at Goodison for the club as part of a famous hat-trick in 1980 against which team?

789 In 1977/78 who started off the season in goals and played 98 consecutive League games?

790 In 1980/81 who took over the number nine jersey from Bob Latchford halfway through the season?

791 Who was the club's top League scorer in 1979/80 season?

792 At which park did Kevin Ratcliffe make his League debut for Everton?

BLUES IN THE FA CUP— THE SIXTIES AND SEVENTIES

793 Who beat Everton in the 1968 FA Cup final?

794 In 1967 Alan Ball made his Everton Cup debut in a third round 0-0 draw against which team?

795 In the 1967 Cup, Everton lost 2-3 in the sixth round to Nottingham Forest. Who scored both Everton's goals in that match?

796 Who did Everton beat 1-0 in the 1968 Cup semi-final?

797 In the 1968 Cup final who scored the only goal of the game in extra time to beat Everton 0-1?

798 In the 1969 Cup which player scored in every round except the semi-final?

799 Who beat Everton in the 1969 semi-final and went on to win the Cup?

800 In 1971 who did Everton beat 5-0 in the quarter-finals of the Cup?

801 When Everton lost 1-2 at Derby in the third round of the 1976 FA Cup who scored his only Cup goal for the Blues in that match?

802 In the 1975 FA Cup, which Cinderella team came to Goodison in the third round and got a 1-1 draw?

803 When Everton beat Liverpool 1-0 in the fifth round of the 1967 FA Cup, who scored the goal?

804 In the 1968 FA Cup, Everton beat three teams from the lower Leagues in rounds three, four and five without losing a goal. Name any of the opposing teams?

805 Who scored Everton's goal when they beat Leeds 1-0 in the 1968 Cup semi-final?

806 In the 1969 Cup, Everton beat Coventry and Ipswich in the third and fourth rounds, scoring twice in each game. The same players scored the goals. Can you name them?

807 Which second division team beat Everton 1-2 at Goodison in the fourth round of the Cup in 1975?

808 Who did Everton beat in the 1969 FA Cup quarter-finals?

809 When Everton went to Old Trafford and won a third round replay by 2-0 in the 1975 FA Cup, which two players got the goals?

810 In 1971 Everton lost 1-2 in the semi-final of the Cup to Liverpool. Name all the scorers in that match?

811 The fourth round of 1973 was another Cup shocker for Everton as they went down 0-2 to which team at Goodison?

812 In 1975 Everton beat Derby 1-0 in the fifth round, and the scorer was making his Cup debut for Everton. It was also his only Cup appearance that season. Who was the player?

813 Name this former Goodison hero?
814 Which two teams did he play for after Everton?
815 Who was the Everton manager who sold him?
816 Against which team did he play his last senior match?

817 In which season did Everton first play in the League Cup?

818 In the 1973/74 Cup, Everton lost 0-1 at Goodison in round three to a team they took seven goals off in the League. Who were they?

819 In the 1978/79 Cup who did Everton beat 8-0 in the second round?

820 In that match, who got five goals and who got a hat-trick?

821 In the third round of the 1979/80 Cup who did Everton beat 4-1 at Goodison after a 0-0 draw?

822 In 1982/83 Everton drew with Arsenal 1-1 at Goodison. Who scored to give the Blues a replay?

823 In the first leg of the 1983/84 semi-final against Aston Villa Everton won 2-0. Who were the scorers?

824 Which second division team beat Everton 0-2 in a fourth round replay in the 1975/76 Cup?

825 In the 1980/81 Cup who did Everton beat 5-2 on aggregate in the second round?

826 In the second round in 1981/82 Everton beat Coventry 2-1 on aggregate. Who scored a goal in each leg for Everton?

827 In the 1967/68 Cup Everton beat Bristol City 5-0 in the second round. Which famous Evertonian got a double in that match?

828 Who beat Everton 0-1 in one of the second round matches in 1979/80, but the Blues got through 2-1 on aggregate?

829 In 1982/83 when Everton lost a replay in the third round to Arsenal, what was the score?

830 When Everton beat Oxford 1-0 at Goodison in the 1981/82 third round, who scored the Blues goal?

831 In the 1975/76 Cup Everton won 1-0 away after a 2-2 draw at Goodison in the second round against a team they did not beat in the League between 1975 and 1977. Which team?

832 When Everton lost the 1977 final to Aston Villa the three matches were played at different venues. Name them?

833 Who beat Everton 2-3 at Goodison in the 1978/79 fourth round?

834 Who captained the 1984 Cup final team?

A happy Neville Southall, one of the best goalkeepers in the world.

835 In the third round in 1985/86 who did Everton beat 4-1?

836 Who did Everton beat 6-2 on aggregate in the second round in 1984/85?

Due to the aftermath of the Heysel Disaster, Everton did not appear in Europe as League champions, but at home the action was furious as the Blues finished second in the League and lost at the final hurdle in the FA Cup. It was a season of consolidation for the club, who were now cast as the best team in England.

837 Who came to the club in a storm of publicity and ended the season as top goalscorer?

838 In the fifth round of the FA Cup Everton had a great 2-1 win over which team away from home?

839 Gary Lineker's first hat-trick for Everton came at Goodison in an early League match against which team?

840 Name the youngster who emerged to play occasionally in the first team wearing the number five jersey?

841 The only League game Lineker missed was against Ipswich when Everton won 1-0 near the end of the season. Who wore the number eight jersey in that match?

842 An own-goal from which opposition player gave Everton a 2-2 draw and the right to a replay in the FA Cup sixth round?

843 Who played in goal for the Blues in the FA Cup final?

844 Who were the opposition when Everton were taken to a replay in the FA Cup sixth round?

845 Everton had a great 2-0 win over Liverpool at Anfield in the League. Who were the two players who scored the goals?

846 In the FA Cup semi-final when the Blues beat Sheffield Wednesday 2-1 who were Everton's goalscorers?

847 Name the two players who made their League debut in the last game of the season against West Ham?

848 Name the young player who made his first team debut in the Screen Sport Super Cup and played both semi-final legs?

Gary Stevens — the action man in action.

849 Who beat Everton 1-2 at Goodison in the League Cup fourth round?

850 Name all the scorers in the FA Cup final when Liverpool beat Everton 1-3?

851 Against which team in the League Cup did Ian Marshall get his first Everton goal?

852 In January 1986 he came on as a substitute for Kevin Sheedy and scored his only goal of the season, the winner in the 4-3 match against Queens Park Rangers. Who?

853 Who did Everton beat 1-0 in the FA Cup third round?

854 Name the players who scored Chelsea's goals to put the Blues out of the League Cup?

855 Whose own goal gave Everton a 1-0 win over Manchester United in the Screen Sport Super Cup?

856 Who did Everton beat in the final of the Screen Sport Super Cup?

INTERNATIONAL BLUES (I)

857 Against which team did Alan Ball win his first cap as an Everton player?

858 His only Scotland cap came in 1973 against Switzerland. Who was the player?

859 Against which country did Brian Labone win his last England cap?

860 Ted Sagar won two caps against foreign opposition, both of whom beat England. Name either country?

861 A big star with Glasgow Rangers, his five Scotland caps were won while an Everton player. Who was he?

862 Where and against which country did Ray Wilson win his last England cap?

863 Gordon West kept one clean sheet in three England outings, against who?

864 How many caps did Tommy Lawton win as an Everton player?

865 Joe Royle's only England goal as an Everton player earned his country a 1-1 draw with which team?

866 Who was the first player to score against Neville Southall in an international match?

867 Who was the first Everton player to score for England?

868 Who was the first Everton player to be capped for Scotland?

869 What was Alan Ball's goals total for England?

870 The only time Bob Latchford scored a double for England was in 1979 at Wembley. Who were the opposition?

871 Which two players were the first from Everton to be capped for England?

872 He was one of Scotland's Wembley Wizards in 1928 and later won two caps as an Everton player. Who was he?

873 Who was the first Everton player capped by Ireland?

874 What club was Tommy Lawton with when he won his last England cap?

875 Who scored a hat-trick on his England debut in 1964?

876 Who were the first two Everton players capped for Wales?

877 No prizes for naming this man?

878 In which year did he make his famous debut?

879 Against which country did he win his only England cap?

880 What job was he promoted to in 1983?

881 Whose career ended in 1980 after he sustained a shattered knee in a tackle with Liverpool's Jimmy Case?

882 Who took over as regular goalkeeper for Northern Ireland after Billy Scott?

883 Which Everton player won the 1985 PFA Player of the Year award?

884 Name the two brothers who played for Everton in the 1907 FA Cup final?

885 Where did Stan Bentham coach after leaving Everton in 1962?

886 Which former Everton manager played in the 1959 FA Cup final?

887 Which old Evertonian had one leg shorter than the other?

888 Who was Billy Bingham's first signing for Everton?

889 Who won a Scottish Cup winners medal and an English Cup winners medal in the space of three years in the thirties?

890 Johnny Carey was manager of which club before Everton?

891 Where did Billy Bingham go after he left Everton as manager of the club?

892 Which two clubs did Johnny Carey manage after Everton?

893 Which country beat England 1-2 at Goodison in 1949, with two Everton players in their side, to become the first 'foreign' team to win on English soil?

894 What trade did Tommy Eglinton pursue when he gave up football?

895 Which old Evertonian was once the youngest player to appear in a League match?

896 What was Andy Gray's first senior team?

897 Who was appointed Youth coach of Everton in 1976?

898 Who had two spells as a player with Everton with a ten-year gap in between?

899 Which Everton goalkeeper once could not get a place with the now defunct Bradford Park Avenue?

900 Which two Everton players represented England at both football and cricket?

901 He was capped twice for England, once against the Rest of Europe in 1938. Who was he?

902 Against which team did Ray Wilson win his first England cap as an Everton player?

903 Which Everton player has been capped most times for Wales?

904 Name the Everton player who was capped 27 times for Eire and seven times for Northern Ireland?

905 How many caps did Billy Scott win while an Everton player?

906 What scoring record did Dixie Dean create in his first five England matches?

907 Against which country did Colin Harvey win his only England cap in 1971?

908 Who scored on his Scotland debut in 1896 as Scotland beat England 2-1?

909 Who was the only Everton goalkeeper to play for Scotland?

910 In 1974/75 he won as many Welsh caps as he played games for Everton. Who?

911 When Fred Pickering got a hat-trick in his first England match against the USA what was the final score?

912 How many England goals did Bob Latchford score?

913 In 1985 Scotland paired Everton strikers Andy Gray and Graeme Sharp against which country?

914 Who were the opposition in Dai Davies' last Welsh appearance as an Everton player?

915 Paul Bracewell won his first England cap against West Germany as a substitute. Who did he replace and where was the game played?

916 Fred Pickering was capped three times. In how many did he score?

917 Who was the only Everton player to appear against Trinidad and Tobago in a full international?

918 Apart from Wally Boyes which other Everton player was capped for England against the Rest of Europe in 1938?

919 Which Everton player represented Scotland in the 1958 World Cup?

920 How many goals did Dixie Dean score for England?

921 Who provided the opposition when Roy Vernon made his senior football debut with Blackburn Rovers?

922 Who has been connected with Everton for over fifty years in various posts, including player, trainer and promotions officer?

923 Which Everton player turned down the job of youth team coach under Gordon Lee?

924 An injury to which player gave Charlie Gee the chance for stardom?

925 Who left Everton when Mickey Walsh arrived?

926 Which Scottish club did Joe Donnachie once play for?

927 What tragic ailment caused Mark Higgins to quit football?

928 Name the Scots centre-half who signed for Everton in 1972 at the age of 16?

929 Who at Goodison was called The India Rubber Man?

930 Which player went to Huddersfield as part of the deal which brought Ray Wilson to Everton?

931 Who did Bobby Parker replace as Everton's striker in 1913?

932 Who came to Everton in 1984 after playing for seven other senior clubs?

933 Why did Gordon Dugdale have to give up football?

934 Where was Trevor Steven born?

935 Ian Bishop once went on loan from Everton to which team?

936 Warren Aspinall joined Everton from which team?

937 With which famous Glasgow nursery team did Graeme Sharp once play?

938 From which club did Paul Wilkinson join Everton?

939 Neville Southall was once loaned by Everton to which team?

940 Which former Everton player once stood for Parliament?

BLUES IN THE LEAGUE CUP (2)

941 What team beat Everton 0-1 in a fourth round replay in 1968/69?

942 Who did Everton beat 3-1 in their first League Cup match?

943 Who scored to give Everton a precarious 1-0 win in the 1976/77 Cup against Stockport in the third round?

Paul Power thunders one past the outstretched Kenny Clements of Manchester City.

944 Who beat Everton in a replayed 1984 final at Maine Road?

945 When Everton lost 2-3 at Goodison to Ipswich in the 1981/82 Cup, which player got both Everton's goals?

946 Which third division team beat Everton 1-2 in the 1979/80 Cup?

947 Who beat Everton 1-2 in the fifth round of the 1960/61 Cup?

948 In 1983/84 who played in every League Cup tie except the final replay?

949 Which team put Everton out of the 1967/68 Cup by 2-3 at Goodison, and who got both Everton's goals in that third round match?

950 Who did Everton beat 2-0 in the second round first leg in 1982/83 in a match that was Neville Southall's League Cup debut?

951 In the fourth round of the 1985/86 Cup Everton drew 2-2 with Chelsea at Stamford Bridge. Who were Everton's scorers?

952 Who was Everton's substitute at Wembley in the 1984 final against Liverpool?

953 Who did Everton beat 2-1 away from home in the 1984/85 third round?

954 Who got the goal when Everton beat Arsenal 1-0 at Goodison in a third round replay in the 1969/70 Cup?

955 In the 1971/72 Cup Everton lost 1-2 in the second round to Southampton. Who became the first Everton player in two years to get a League Cup goal in that match?

956 In 1974/75 Aston Villa beat Everton 0-3 after a 1-1 draw in the second round. Who scored Everton's goal in the first match?

957 In 1976/77 who were the only team to score against Everton in the Cup until the final?

958 In the 1977/78 Cup his only appearance that season was as a substitute against Middlesbrough and he scored to give Everton a 2-2 draw and a replay. Who was the player?

959 In the third round in 1978/79 a Martin Dobson goal gave Everton a lucky win against which small team?

960 Who got a rare goal for Everton, his only one for the club in the League Cup, when the team lost 1-2 at Goodison to West Bromwich in the 1980/81 third round?

BLUES IN THE FA CUP—THE EIGHTIES

961 When Everton beat Aldershot 4-1 in the third round of the Cup in 1980 which famous Scottish internationalist scored his first Cup goal for the Blues in that match?

962 When Everton beat Liverpool 2-1 in the fourth round in 1981, which two players scored for the Blues?

963 In the third round in 1983, Everton were taken to a surprise replay by which team?

964 Everton lost at West Ham by 1-2 in the third round in 1982. Who scored for the Blues in that game?

965 In 1983, who did the Blues beat 2-0 in the fifth round with goals from King and Sharp?

Graeme Sharp, fearless as ever, attacks the Norwich defence.

966 When Everton won the Cup in 1984, who came into the side at the semi-final stage and played in the final?

967 And in 1984, who played in every Cup tie, scored two goals and missed the final?

968 In 1985 Everton drew 2-2 at Goodison in the sixth round but won the replay 1-0. Who were the opposing team, and who scored the vital goal which took Everton through?

969 In the fourth round in 1986 when Everton beat Blackburn 3-1 who scored for both teams?

970 In 1979 Everton lost 1-2 at the first try to which team?

971 In the 1986 Cup final, name Everton's substitute and the player he came on for?

972 In 1980 when Everton beat Ipswich 2-1 in the quarter-finals, which two players scored the Everton goals?

973 In 1983 who scored his first Cup goal for Everton in the surprise 1-1 draw with Newport in the third round?

974 Who beat Everton in the 1983 quarter-finals by 0-1?

975 Who scored the first goal of the 1986 Cup campaign to set the club on the way to Wembley. The opposition was Stoke City?

976 Who beat Everton in the 1980 Cup semi-final?

977 In the fifth round of the 1981 Cup, Everton beat Southampton 1-0 in a replay at Goodison. Who scored his only Cup goal for Everton that night?

978 Where was the 1980 Cup semi-final replay with West Ham held when Everton lost 1-2?

978 In 1981 which team beat Everton 1-3 in a sixth round replay?

980 And finally, who played a record 56 FA Cup ties for Everton?

SOME EARLY HISTORY

981 The club was first formed, connected with which church?

982 The name Everton was adopted at a meeting in which hotel?

983 What was the score in Everton's first-ever match against St Peters?

984 Everton's first opponents in the Lancashire Cup beat the club by 1-8 in a replay. Who were they?

985 Name the Scot who was elected club captain early in their history and was later club coach?

986 What were the colours of Everton's original jerseys?

987 To gain uniformity, Everton dyed all their strips which colour?

988 Which team beat Everton 1-13 in a fixture in 1881?

989 Everton won their first trophy in 1884. What was it?

990 And who did they beat in that memorable final?

991 In their first season at Goodison, the visit of which team gave Everton a then record 30,000 crowd?

992 Who initiated Everton's move to Goodison after the split with John Houlding?

993 In September 1884 Everton played their first match at which ground?

One of the best-loved players ever at Everton — Kevin Sheedy.

994 In 1904 the club signed a Welsh international goalkeeper. Who was he?

995 In 1895 George Mahon resigned, but who was elected to the board to start a 50-year love affair with the club?

996 What was Goodison Park known as locally when the club first moved to it?

997 Who were Everton's first two professional players?

998 The first time Everton were in the FA Cup proper they lost 0-6 to Preston, but why was the match a waste of time?

999 What was the club's early headquarters and dressing rooms?

1000 What was George Mahon's connection with Everton's roots?

1001 In 1894 the FA Cup final was played at Goodison. Which two teams took part?

Answers

1 It was scored direct from a corner.
2 £840,000.
3 Graeme Sharp.
4 Manchester City.
5 Derek Mountfield against Watford (two for Everton one for Watford).
6 Paul Wilkinson, Ian Snodin.
7 Laurie Madden.
8 It was their first victory on an artificial pitch.
9 Nottingham Forest.
10 He refused permission for Dave Watson to play, as he had played against both clubs in the tournament the previous season.
11 Adrian Heath.
12 It was the first of his career.
13 £1.2 million.
14 Paul Wilkinson, 9-1.
15 Ian Snodin.
16 Nottingham Forest.
17 Mike Newell.
18 Newcastle, Leicester.
19 A topless girl appeared on the park!.
20 Southampton (2-1).

21 Bobby Parker (36).
22 Queens Park Rangers.
23 Burnley or Blackburn Rovers.
24 Tom Fern.
25 William Brown.
26 Barnsley.
27 Villa Park.
28 John Macconnachie.

29 Tom Fleetwood.
30 Oldham.
31 Jimmy Galt.
32 Bristol City.
33 Sheffield Wednesday in Sheffield.
34 Six times.
35 Chelsea.
36 Jimmy Galt.
37 Joe Clennell.
38 Stamford Bridge.
39 Bradford City.
40 Chelsea.

THE LEAGUE CAMPAIGNS—THE EARLY YEARS ANSWERS

41 G. Fleming.
42 Fred Geary.
43 Alex Latta.
44 Alf Milward.
45 John Bell.
46 Eleventh.
47 Jack Southworth.
48 11.
49 18.
50 Aston Villa.
51 Scoring in six consecutive League matches.
52 Six.
53 Derby.
54 Jimmy Settle.
55 Jack Southworth.
56 Derby.
57 Edgar and Arthur Chadwick.
58 3-0 for Everton.
59 A. McKinnon.
60 They won their first six games.

61 Club chairman, Dick Seale.

62 Newcastle.

63 Dixie Dean.

64 Morton.

65 Bertie Freeman (Burnley).

66 Dave Hickson (Huddersfield and Liverpool).

67 Brian Kidd (Manchester United).

68 Jack Sharp.

69 Nick Ross.

70 Liverpool.

71 Duggie Livingstone.

72 It was at centre-half, a position he had never played in for Everton.

73 Croydon Common.

74 Dave Clements.

75 Buenos Aires.

76 Ephraim.

77 Jimmy Husband.

78 Tom Booth.

79 Bryan Hamilton (Freight Rover Trophy).

80 An American baseball match.

REMEMBER THIS SEASON—1931/32
ANSWERS

81 45.

82 They scored 28 times in those matches.

83 Jimmy Dunn.

84 Ted Sagar.

85 Billy Coggins.

86 Arsenal.

87 Tommy Johnson.

88 Sheffield Wednesday, Chelsea.

89 Sheffield Wednesday, Leicester.

90 Ben Williams, Warney Cresswell.
91 Ted Critchley, Jimmy Stein.
92 George Martin.
93 Charlie Gee.
94 Liverpool.
95 Dixie Dean.
96 It was their highest-ever total in the first division (116).
97 Ten times.
98 Manchester City, Arsenal.
99 Blackburn Rovers.
100 Tommy White v Portsmouth in the second match of the season.

PICTURE QUIZ (I)
ANSWERS

101 Howard Kendall.
102 Preston.
103 1981.
104 Southampton.

WHERE DID THEY COME FROM (I)
ANSWERS

105 Blackburn Rovers.
106 Sheffield Wednesday.
107 Sheffield Wednesday.
108 Anderlecht, 1976, £200,000.
109 Tommy Jackson.
110 Dumbarton.
111 Colin Todd from Derby County.
112 Sunderland.
113 Newcastle.
114 Glasgow Rangers.
115 1975, £40,000, Ipswich.
116 Barnsley.
117 Blackburn Rovers.

118 Partick Thistle.

119 Chelsea.

120 Charlton Athletic.

121 Port Sunlight.

122 January 1982, £700,000, Stoke City.

123 Dunmurry.

124 David Lawson from Huddersfield.

SOME CLUB FACTS
ANSWERS

125 Philip Carter.

126 Stanley Park.

127 4-10 v Spurs in 1958.

128 121 (1930/31).

129 Alan Ball.

130 Ted Sagar (465).

131 St Peter's.

132 1962/63.

133 Priory Road.

134 Accrington.

135 Eighth.

136 Four seasons.

137 Jim Greenwood.

138 11-2 v Derby in 1889/90.

139 1890/91.

140 1892.

141 Theo Kelly.

142 Bolton Wanderers.

143 Edgar Chadwick.

144 1906.

REMEMBER THIS SEASON 1938/39
ANSWERS

145 Tommy Lawton.

146 Doncaster.

147 Wolves.

148 Tommy G. Jones.

149 Cliff Britton.
150 Torry Gillick v Aston Villa.
151 Theo Kelly.
152 Norman Greenhalgh.
153 Birmingham.
154 Middlesbrough.
155 Charlton.
156 Wally Boyes.
157 Norman Greenhalgh.
158 Wolverhampton.
159 Gordon Watson.
160 Torry Gillick.
161 Wolves.
162 Stan Bentham.
163 It was a club record for the first division.
164 Jimmy Caskie, Glasgow Rangers.

WHERE DID THEY GO (1)
ANSWERS

165 Glentoran.
166 Oldham Athletic.
167 Notts County.
168 Peter Eastoe.
169 Breda (Holland).
170 Manchester City for £350,000.
171 Hibernian.
172 Swindon Town.
173 Stoke City.
174 Roger Kenyon.
175 New Brighton Tower.
176 Aston Villa for £250,000.
177 Luton Town.
178 Exeter City.
179 Hibernian, 1974, £120,000.
180 Grimsby.

181 Sheffield Wednesday.
182 Leeds City.
183 Brighton, £400,000.
184 Portsmouth.

185 Newcastle.
186 Joe Clennell.
187 Jack Southworth.
188 Walter Scott.
189 Bertie Freeman.
190 John MacDonald.
191 Jack Cock.
192 Nottingham Forest.
193 Middlesbrough.
194 Notts County.
195 3-0.
196 Inside-right.
197 Bury.
198 Sixteenth.
199 Jack Cock.
200 Tom Fern.
201 Manchester City.
202 Newcastle.
203 Bertie Freeman.
204 Charlie Crossley.

205 Kevin Ratcliffe.
206 FA Cup, Charity Shield, League championship, Cup Winners Cup.
207 Manchester United.
208 Ipswich.

209 The Inter-Cities Fairs Cup.
210 Dunfermline Athletic.
211 1-2.
212 0-1.
213 Valerengen.
214 Ujpest Doza.
215 Kilmarnock.
216 Andy Rankin.
217 IFC Nuremburg.
218 Dennis Stevens.
219 Colin Harvey.
220 9-4.
221 Manchester United.
222 Fred Pickering.
223 Brian Harris.
224 Fred Pickering.
225 0-3.
226 Alan Ball.
227 Aalborg.
228 George Thomson.

SEASON 1962/63
ANSWERS

229 Roy Vernon.
230 Tottenham Hotspur.
231 Albert Dunlop.
232 Alex Scott.
233 West Ham.
234 He wore a number seven jersey for one of the few times in his career.
235 Wignall.
236 Tony Kay.
237 Manchester United.

238 Derek Temple.
239 West Bromwich.
240 Fulham.
241 Swindon.
242 Dennis Stevens, Alex Young.
243 None.
244 61.
245 There were no games because of severe weather for eight weeks.
246 Alex Scott.
247 Alex Young.
248 Roy Vernon.

WHERE DID THEY COME FROM (2) ANSWERS

249 £110,000.
250 St Johnstone, £75,000.
251 Lincoln City.
252 Queens Park.
253 Dundee.
254 Stockport County.
255 Huddersfield.
256 Glasgow Rangers.
257 Manchester City.
258 Burnley.
259 1977, £150,000.
260 Bootle.
261 £140,000.
262 Belfast Celtic.
263 Sunderland, £240,000.
264 Celtic, £39,000.
265 Charlie Crossley.
266 Airdrieonians.
267 Hibernian.
268 Stockport County.

269 Birmingham.

270 Port Vale.

271 Preston.

272 Third Lanark.

273 Burnley.

274 Aston Villa for £17,500.

275 1967, Birminhgam.

276 Manchester City in 1975.

277 Bolton, 1980, £150,000.

278 1983, Aston Villa, £250,000.

279 Burnley.

280 Alan Whittle.

281 Burnley.

282 Leeds United.

283 Tom Fleetwood.

284 Aston Villa, £150,000.

285 1976, Oldham.

286 Arsenal for £7000.

287 Oldham.

288 Newcastle.

PICTURE QUIZ (3)
ANSWERS

289 Peter Reid.

290 Bolton.

291 £60,000.

292 The 1984 Milk Cup final.

REMEMBER THIS SEASON—1965/66

293 Eleventh.

294 John Hurst.

295 Fred Pickering.
296 He received a World Cup winners medal.
297 Bedford Town.
298 Burnden Park, Bolton.
299 Mike Trebilcock (2), Derek Temple.
300 Sheffield Wednesday.
301 Fred Pickering.
302 Coventry.
303 Andy Rankin, Geoff Barnett.
304 Sunderland.
305 Liverpool.
306 Harris, Harvey, Labone, Scott, Temple, West, Young.
307 Tommy Wright.
308 McCalliog, Ford.
309 Manchester City.
310 Colin Harvey.
311 Mike Trebilcock.
312 Fred Pickering.

BLUES IN THE FA CUP—THE EARLY YEARS
ANSWERS

313 Bolton Wanderers.
314 Wolves.
315 Fallowfield, Manchester.
316 John Bell in 1897.
317 Derby County.
318 In 1902 Everton lost 0-2 at Goodison after a 2-2 draw at Anfield.
319 Newcastle.
320 Sandy Young.
321 Preston.
322 Glasgow Rangers.
323 Brady, Geary and Milward.
324 Jack Taylor.
325 Sheffield Wednesday.

326 Jack Sharp.
327 Sheffield Wednesday, in round three.
328 Liverpool.
329 Victoria Ground, Stoke; Trent Bridge, Nottingham.
330 Preston.
331 Aston Villa.
332 Crystal Palace.

333 Aston Villa.
334 1927/28.
335 Manchester City.
336 Derby.
337 Arsenal.
338 Billy Coggins.
339 4-7.
340 32.
341 Jimmy Stein.
342 He played less than half the season at centre forward and only
    28 games in all.
343 Alec Troup.
344 Hunter Hart.
345 45.
346 Dick Forshaw.
347 Jimmy Stein.
348 Burnley at Turf Moor.
349 Manchester United.
350 Twentieth, eighteenth.
351 They were relegated.
352 Tommy White.

353 Undertaker.
354 George Martin.
355 Jack Cock.
356 Farnworth.
357 Stoke.
358 Liverpool, Spurs and Ipswich.
359 Martin Dobson.
360 Albert Dunlop.
361 Fort Lauderdale.
362 Tommy Lawton.
363 Billy.
364 Billy Bingham.
365 Alan Durban.
366 Harold Hardman.
367 Celtic.
368 Neil Robinson.
369 Tom Clinton.
370 Nat.
371 Barrow.
372 16.

PICTURE QUIZ (4)
ANSWERS

373 Gary Stevens.
374 1979.
375 Italy.
376 West Ham.

377 Joe Royle.

378 Nine points.

379 66.

380 Darlington.

381 Brian Labone, Gordon West.

382 Liverpool (0-3 League match).

383 Manchester City.

384 Nottingham Forest.

385 Alan Whittle.

386 Leeds.

387 Keith Newton, Tommy Wright, Brian Labone, Alan Ball.

388 Sandy Brown.

389 Sheffield United.

390 Keith Newton.

391 Arsenal.

392 Jimmy Husband.

393 They won eight consecutive games and went fourteen undefeated.

394 Roger Kenyon.

395 Alan Ball.

396 Alan Ball (v Sheffield United, Darlington) Howard Kendall (v Arsenal).

397 Sheffield United.

398 Southampton.

399 Luton.

400 Hibernian.

401 1982, £60,000. Bolton Wanderers.

402 Small Heath.

403 Derby County.

404 Bristol Rovers.

405 Jimmy Caskie.
406 Wolves, Coventry.
407 Nottingham Forest.
408 Adlington.
409 Glasgow Rangers.
410 John Gidman.
411 £180,000.
412 Dunfermline.
413 Wrexham.
414 Bob Latchford, Birmingham.
415 Sunderland.
416 Burnell's Ironworks.

BLUES IN THE FA CUP—AROUND TWO WARS ANSWERS

417 Scott, Balmer, Crelley, Makepeace, Taylor, Abbott, Sharp, Bolton, Young, Settle, Hardman.
418 Browell.
419 Poole Town.
420 Southport.
421 West Bromwich.
422 Barnsley.
423 Glossop.
424 Crystal Palace.
425 Crystal Palace, Southport.
426 Fulham.
427 Tottenham.
428 Jackie Coulter.
429 Chelsea.
430 Birmingham.
431 West Ham, Molyneux.
432 Manchester City.
433 Dixie Dean, Jimmy Dunn, Jimmy Stein.
434 White shirts.
435 They were numbered (1-22!).
436 Dixie Dean.

437 Sunderland.
438 2-7.
439 Jock Dodds.
440 Wolves.
441 Eleven.
442 Tommy G. Jones.
443 Leicester City.
444 Derek Temple.
445 32 points.
446 They managed only eight away goals.
447 Arsenal.
448 Torry Gillick.
449 Tenth.
450 Harry Catterick.
451 Albert Dunlop.
452 Ted Sagar.
453 Jimmy Harris.
454 Sixteenth.
455 They did it together, against Burnley in 1955.
456 Sheffield Wednesday.

PICTURE QUIZ (5)
ANSWERS

457 Derek Mountfield.
458 Tranmere Rovers.
459 £30,000.
460 Mark Higgins.

REMEMBER THIS SEASON 1976/77
ANSWERS

461 Gordon Lee took over from Billy Bingham.

462 Ninth.
463 Coventry.
464 Manchester United.
465 Liverpool.
466 Mike Bernard, David Jones, Neil Robinson.
467 Mike Pejic.
468 Bob Latchford.
469 Bob Latchford.
470 Roger Kenyon.
471 Ken McNaught.
472 Swindon.
473 Duncan Mackenzie.
474 Duncan McKenzie, Bruce Rioch.
475 Dai Davies, David Lawson, Drew Brand.
476 Bolton.
477 2-3.
478 Little (2), Nicholl.
479 Derby.
480 Bob Latchford, Mick Lyons.

481 Notts County and Scunthorpe.
482 Cardiff City.
483 Martin Dobson, who returned to Burnley.
484 Bolton Wanderers.
485 Plymouth.
486 Wrexham.
487 Steve Coppell, then of Crystal Palace.
488 Chesterfield, £10,000.
489 Burnley.
490 Ardwick.
491 Watford.
492 AEK Athens.
493 1965, Oldham.
494 Oldham.

495 San Diego.
496 £220,000 to Arsenal.
497 Queens Park Rangers.
498 Tom Fern.
499 Ron Atkinson.
500 1945, Chelsea, £11,500.

501 Harry Catterick.
502 John Gidman.
503 Jimmy Husband.
504 Tommy Docherty.
505 Blackpool.
506 Billy Cook.
507 George Brewster (Brooklands Athletic).
508 The League Cup.
509 Neville Southall.
510 Ron and George Saunders.
511 George Telfer.
512 Blackburn.
513 Dave Clements.
514 Huddersfield.
515 Torrance.
516 20.
517 Italy.
518 Burnley.
519 Neil McBain.
520 Alex Scott (then with Rangers).

521 None did.

522 Bobby Collins.
523 Third.
524 Joe Royle.
525 Tommy Ring.
526 Jimmy Harris.
527 Roy Vernon.
528 Jimmy Gabriel.
529 Alan Ball.
530 Billy Bingham.
531 Huddersfield.
532 Fred Pickering.
533 Tommy Wright.
534 Tottenham.
535 Anfield.
536 Cardiff City.
537 Newcastle.
538 Gordon West.
539 Brian Labone, Blackburn Rovers.
540 Birmingham.

PICTURE QUIZ (6) ANSWERS

541 Trevor Steven.
542 Burnley.
543 Northern Ireland.
544 1983.

THE BLUES IN EUROPE—THE SIXTIES AND SEVENTIES ANSWERS

545 Real Zaragoza.
546 Alan Ball v Keflavik.

547 Alan Whittle v Keflavik.
548 Borussia Munchengladbach.
549 Panathanaikos.
550 0-1.
551 Finn Harps.
552 5-0, 5-0.
553 Dukla Prague.
554 Joe McBride.
555 AC Milan, 1975.
556 Sandy Brown.
557 Ball (3), Royle (2), Kendall.
558 Royle (2), Whittle.
559 David Johnson.
560 European Cup first round first leg v Keflavik 1970.
561 David Lawson, Dai Davies.
562 Andy King, Bob Latchford.
563 Feyenoord.
564 Brian Labone, Colin Harvey.

REMEMBER THIS SEASON 1977/78
ANSWERS

565 Third.
566 76.
567 Aston Villa.
568 George Wood.
569 Sheffield Wednesday.
570 Bruce Rioch.
571 Bob Latchford.
572 Dave Thomas.
573 Queens Park Rangers.
574 Duncan McKenzie.
575 Middlesbrough.
576 Trevor Ross.
577 George Wood, Andy King, Mick Lyons.
578 Leeds.
579 Dave Thomas.

580 Mark Higgins.
581 Middlesbrough.
582 Billy Wright.
583 Manchester United.
584 15.

585 1965 from Plymouth.
586 Preston.
587 Manchester United.
588 Falkirk.
589 Martin Dobson from Burnley.
590 Shelbourne.
591 Wolves, Swindon, Queens Park Rangers.
592 Jimmy Galt.
593 Dundee United, Aston Villa, Wolves.
594 Blackburn Rovers.
595 Millwall Athletic.
596 West Bromwich Albion.
597 Dundalk.
598 Tommy Eglinton and Peter Farrell.
599 Bradford City.
600 Blackpool.
601 1979, £150,000, Manchester City.
602 Alex Scott from Rangers.
603 Rochdale.
604 Wigan, in 1934.

WHERE DID THEY GO (4)
ANSWERS

605 Portsmouth.
606 1977, £200,000.

607 Southport.

608 Swansea.

609 Derby in 1973 for £110,000.

610 Huddersfield.

611 Birmingham, £110,000.

612 Chelsea.

613 Wolves.

614 Tulsa Roughnecks.

615 Exeter City.

616 1977.

617 Sunderland.

618 1967 to Preston for £35,000.

619 Tottenham Hotspur.

620 David Lawson.

621 Birmingham City.

622 1967, Southampton.

623 Fred Geary.

624 Birmingham City, £275,000.

PICTURE QUIZ (7)
ANSWERS

625 William 'Dixie' Dean.

626 Sligo.

627 14.

628 In a motorbike accident.

BLUES IN THE CUP—FROM THE THIRTIES TO THE SIXTIES
ANSWERS

629 Wolves.

630 Torry Gillick against Birmingham.

631 The Cup that year was played on a two leg basis.

632 King's Lynn, Billy Bingham.

633 Harry Catterick.

634 Bolton.

635 In 1950, 1953, 1956 and 1957 they went out of the Cup each time in Manchester.

636 Bradford City.

637 Sunderland.

638 Sheffield Wednesday.

639 Dave Hickson.

640 John Willie Parker.

641 None.

642 Bob Paisley and Billy Liddell.

643 Torry Gillick and Alex Stevenson, both played with Glasgow Rangers.

644 Liverpool.

645 Fred Pickering.

646 Tommy Lawton.

647 Leeds.

648 Derek Temple.

REMEMBER THIS SEASON—1983/84 ANSWERS

649 Gillingham.

650 It was all the Blues had scored in the first half of the League programme.

651 Adrian Heath.

652 Seventh.

653 Notts County, Andy Gray, Kevin Richardson.

654 Southampton at Highbury, Adrian Heath.

655 Andy Gray and Graeme Sharp.

656 Southall, Stevens, Bailey, Ratcliffe, Mountfield, Reid, Steven, Heath, Sharp, Gray, Richardson.

657 Graeme Souness.

658 Oxford.

659 Aston Villa.

660 David Johnson.

661 Robbie Wakenshaw, Ian Bishop.

662 Nottingham Forest.

663 Aston Villa.

664 Mark Higgins.

665 Kevin Sheedy.

666 Alan Harper.

667 Andy King.

668 Against West Ham, League Cup replay, 2-0 at Goodison.

669 Alan Ball.

670 West Bromwich.

671 Sandy Brown.

672 David Lawson.

673 They played all 42 League games.

674 Leicester.

675 Tommy Wright, John Hurst.

676 36.

677 Mike Lyons, Mike Bernard.

678 Rod Belfitt, Joe Harper, David Johnson, Gary Jones, Mick Lyons, Joe Royle.

679 Manchester United.

680 Geoff Barnett.

681 Third.

682 Royle, Harper and Connolly.

683 Alex Young.

684 Southampton.

685 Carlisle.

686 Keith and Henry Newton.

687 Coventry.

688 In four seasons he was the first Everton player to hit double figures.

689 Alex Scott.

690 Belgium.

691 Ian Buchan.

692 Stoke City.

693 Sunderland.

694 Bobby Collins.

695 Terry Kavanagh.

696 He was a baker.

697 A new rule stated that a goal could be scored from a corner but there was no mention that the player could only touch the ball once. He therefore dribbled the ball from the corner spot and scored a goal. The rule was immediately amended.

698 Tommy G. Jones.

699 Wolves.

700 Alfred.

701 Harry Catterick.

702 John Hurst.

703 He won £10,000 from a newspaper.

704 Jimmy Galt (Rangers and Everton).

705 London.

706 Port Vale and Northampton.

707 Cornwall.

708 Jack Southworth.

709 Brian Labone.

710 530.

711 26.

712 1972.

713 Southall, Stevens, Van den Hawe, Ratcliffe, Mountfield, Reid, Steven, Sharp, Gray, Bracewell, Sheedy.

714 Rapid Vienna.

715 Rotterdam.

716 Gray, Sheedy, Steven.

717 Hans Krankl.

718 Graeme Sharp.

719 Inter Bratislava.

720 Paul Bracewell.

721 Heath, Sharp, Sheedy.

722 Czechoslovakia.

723 Andy Gray.

724 Peter Reid, Graeme Sharp.

725 Ian Atkins.

726 0-0.

727 Gray, Sharp, Steven.

728 Pat Van den Hawe.

729 Kevin Ratcliffe.

730 Fred Pickering.

731 Kilmarnock.

732 Feyenoord.

733 13.

734 Paul Wilkinson.

735 Graeme Sharp.

736 Ipswich.

737 Grimsby.

738 Telford.

739 John Bailey.

740 Newcastle.

741 Derek Walsh.

742 University College Dublin.

743 Andy Gray (5).
744 Luton.
745 90.
746 Ten consecutive League wins.
747 Norman Whiteside.
748 Spurs (1-4), Chelsea (3-4).
749 Liverpool.
750 Everton had put them out of the League Cup and beaten them 5-0 in the League.
751 Paul Bracewell.
752 Queens Park Rangers.

WHERE DID THEY COME FROM (5)
ANSWERS

753 Arsenal in 1977.
754 Glasgow Rangers.
755 Blackburn Rovers.
756 1962, for £10,000.
757 Shrewsbury.
758 West Bromwich Albion.
759 New Brighton.
760 Notts County.
761 1907.
762 Huddersfield, Sheffield United, Blackpool.
763 Celtic.
764 Bristol City.
765 1914.
766 Dumbarton.
767 Sunderland, Luton.
768 Partick Thistle.
769 Blackburn Rovers.
770 Richard Boyle.
771 1949, Manchester United.
772 Aberdeen.

773 They went 19 games without defeat.

774 He finished top scorer in the first division.

775 Jim McDonagh.

776 Joe McBride.

777 John Gidman, Garry Stanley.

778 Billy Wright.

779 Left-back.

780 Everton lost 0-5 to Liverpool at Anfield.

781 Birmingham.

782 Ipswich.

783 Coventry, 2-3.

784 Andy King.

785 It was the first time in six years an Everton player had scored three or more in a League match.

786 Birmingham.

787 Peter Eastoe.

788 Crystal Palace.

789 George Wood.

790 Imre Varadi.

791 Brian Kidd.

792 Old Trafford.

793 West Bromwich Albion.

794 Burnley.

795 Jimmy Husband.

796 Leeds United.

797 Geoff Astle.

798 Joe Royle.

799 Manchester City.

800 Colchester.

801 Gary Jones.

802 Altrincham.

803 Alan Ball.

804 Southport, Carlisle, Tranmere.

805 Johnny Morrissey.

806 Joe Royle, John Hurst.

807 Fulham.

808 Manchester United.

809 Bob Latchford, Mick Lyons.

810 Alan Ball, Alun Evans, Brian Hall.

811 Millwall.

812 David Johnson.

813 Alan Ball.

814 Arsenal, Southampton.

815 Harry Catterick.

816 Everton.

817 1960/61.

818 Norwich.

819 Wimbledon.

820 Bob Latchford, Martin Dobson.

821 Aston Villa.

822 Gary Stevens.

823 Kevin Richards and Kevin Sheedy.

824 Notts County.

825 Blackpool.

826 Mick Ferguson.

827 Howard Kendall.
828 Cardiff.
829 0-3.
830 Eammon O'Keefe.
831 Arsenal.
832 Wembley, Hillsborough, Old Trafford.
833 Nottingham Forest.
834 Kevin Ratcliffe.
835 Shrewsbury.
836 Sheffield United.

837 Gary Lineker.
838 Spurs.
839 Birmingham.
840 Ian Marshall.
841 Adrian Heath.
842 Mal Donaghy.
843 Bobby Mimms.
844 Luton Town.
845 Kevin Ratcliffe, Gary Lineker.
846 Harper, Sharp.
847 Peter Billinge, Warren Aspinall.
848 Bobby Coyle.
849 Chelsea.
850 Lineker for Everton, Rush (2), Johnston for Liverpool.
851 Bournemouth.
852 Paul Wilkinson.
853 Exeter.
854 Kerry Dixon, Joe McLaughlin.
855 Frank Stapleton.
856 Spurs.

857 Wales.

858 John Connolly.

859 Against West Germany in the 1970 World Cup in Mexico.

860 Austria, Belgium.

861 Torry Gillick.

862 In Rome against Russia, in the European championships of 1968.

863 Mexico.

864 Eight.

865 Yugoslavia.

866 Terry Butcher.

867 Fred Geary.

868 John Bell.

869 Eight.

870 Northern Ireland.

871 Fred Geary and Johnny Holt, in different matches on the same day!

872 Jimmy Dunn.

873 J. Sheridan.

874 Notts County.

875 Fred Pickering v USA.

876 R. S. Jones and Smart Arridge.

877 Colin Harvey.

878 1963.

879 Malta.

880 First-team coach.

881 Geoff Nulty.

882 His brother Elisha of Liverpool.

883 Peter Reid.

884 Robert and Walter Balmer.

885 Luton Town.

886 Billy Bingham of Luton Town.

887 Wally Boyes.

888 Dave Clements.

889 Billy Cook (Celtic 1931 and Everton 1933).

890 Blackburn.

891 PAOK Salonika, Greece.

892 Nottingham Forest and Leyton Orient.

893 Eire.

894 He was a butcher.

895 Albert Geldard (Bradford), 15 years 156 days.

896 Dundee United.

897 Colin Harvey.

898 David Johnson.

899 David Lawson.

900 Harry Makepeace and Jack Sharp.

INTERNATIONAL BLUES (2)
ANSWERS

901 Wally Boyes.

902 Scotland, 1965.

903 Kevin Ratcliffe.

904 Peter Farrell.

905 16.

906 He scored 12 goals.

907 Malta.

908 John Bell.

909 George Wood.

910 Dave Smallman.

911 10-0.
912 Five.
913 Iceland.
914 Kuwait.
915 Bryan Robson, Mexico City.
916 All three.
917 Mike Walsh (Eire).
918 Tommy Lawton.
919 Alex Parker.
920 18.

MISCELLANEOUS (6)
ANSWERS

921 Liverpool.
922 Gordon Watson.
923 Terry Darracott.
924 Tom Griffiths.
925 John Gidman.
926 Glasgow Rangers.
927 A pelvic disorder.
928 Ken McNaught.
929 Dicky Downs.
930 Mick Meagan.
931 Tom Browell.
932 Terry Curran.
933 He suffered from a heart condition.
934 Berwick.
935 Crewe.
936 Wigan.
937 Eastercraigs.
938 Grimsby.
939 Port Vale.
940 Gordon Dugdale.

BLUES IN THE LEAGUE CUP (2)
ANSWERS

941 Derby.
942 Accrington Stanley.
943 Bob Latchford.
944 Liverpool.
945 Steve McMahon.
946 Grimsby.
947 Shrewsbury.
948 Kevin Sheedy.
949 Sunderland, Alex Young.
950 Newport.
951 Kevin Sheedy, Paul Bracewell.
952 Alan Harper.
953 Manchester United.
954 Howard Kendall.
955 David Johnson.
956 Joe Royle.
957 Bolton Wanderers.
958 George Telfer.
959 Darlington.
960 John Gidman.

BLUES IN THE FA CUP—THE EIGHTIES
ANSWERS

961 Asa Hartford.
962 Peter Eastoe, Imre Varadi.
963 Newport.
964 Peter Eastoe.
965 Spurs.
966 Trevor Steven.
967 Alan Irvine.
968 Ipswich, Graeme Sharp.
969 Pat Van den Hauwe.
970 Sunderland.

971 Adrian Heath, who replaced Gary Stevens.
972 Brian Kidd, Bob Latchford.
973 Kevin Sheedy.
974 Manchester United.
975 Andy Gray.
976 West Ham.
977 Eamonn O'Keefe.
978 Elland Road.
979 Manchester City.
980 Jack Taylor.

SOME EARLY HISTORY
ANSWERS

981 St Domingo's.
982 Queens Head Hotel.
983 6-0.
984 Great Lever.
985 Jack McGill.
986 Blue/white stripes.
987 All black with red sash.
988 Bolton Wanderers.
989 The Liverpool Cup.
990 Earlestown.
991 Preston.
992 George Mahon.
993 Anfield Road.
994 Dr Leigh Richmond-Roose.
995 Will Cuff.
996 Mere Green Field.
997 George Dobson and George Farmer.
998 The FA had already eliminated Everton for illegal payments to players.
999 Sandon Hotel.
1000 He was the organist at St Domingo's.
1001 Notts County and Bolton.